Experiments in Induction

EXPERIMENTS IN INDUCTION

Earl B. Hunt
WESTERN DATA PROCESSING CENTER
THE UNIVERSITY OF CALIFORNIA
LOS ANGELES, CALIFORNIA

Janet Marin
DEPARTMENT OF PSYCHOLOGY
STANFORD UNIVERSITY
STANFORD, CALIFORNIA

Philip J. Stone
LABORATORY OF SOCIAL RELATIONS
HARVARD UNIVERSITY
CAMBRIDGE, MASSACHUSETTS

1966

ACADEMIC PRESS   New York and London

ACADEMIC PRESS INC.
111 Fifth Avenue, New York, New York 10003

United Kingdom Edition published by
ACADEMIC PRESS INC. (LONDON) LTD.
Berkeley Square House, London W.1

LIBRARY OF CONGRESS CATALOG CARD NUMBER: 65-26400

PRINTED IN THE UNITED STATES OF AMERICA

Preface

This book describes an interdisciplinary research project in which computer programs were used to simulate and, in a sense, replace human problem solvers. The research had a dual purpose: to learn more about how people solve complex learning problems and to observe the performance of different varieties of a general learning automaton designed to solve inductive problems which require some learning on the part of the problem solver. The particular tasks which we chose to study all fall into a class of inductive reasoning problems which we call concept learning. The problems are closely related to pattern recognition problems and to problems involving the discovery and utilization of a classification rule.

The book is divided into four parts. Initially, we present a formal characterization of both the problems to be solved and the programming systems used. This provides us with a language we can use to talk about our work. Using this language, we then present accounts of experiments in which different computer programs were used to solve different sorts of concept learning problems. This part of our work can be considered research in artificial intelligence, since the problem-solving abilities of different artificial learners were compared. We next describe experiments in which the performances of some of the programs were compared to the performance of human subjects attacking analogous problems. These experiments are studies in psychology, since the programs, when used in this way, can be regarded as simulations of human thought. In the final chapters we report studies illustrating how our computing techniques can be applied to practical data-processing problems in which it is difficult to use conventional statistical techniques. We confine our attention to classification and discrimination problems which are made difficult by the presence of complex interactions between variables.

Although it is necessarily technical at times, we believe that this book can be read and understood by people who are generally familiar with the "style" of computer programming techniques for data processing, even though they are not experienced programmers. No special knowledge of a particular programming language is required. Similarly, we have been careful not to assume that our readers will have any specific mathematical knowledge, although, again, we do assume that the reader will have some familiarity with the style of mathematical reasoning. To give some content to these remarks, we think that anyone who has had a course in statistical inference or experimental design should be sufficiently conversant with mathematics and statistics to follow our reasoning. Similarly, so would anyone who has had an initial coding course in any computer language.

We hope that our work will be of interest to students and research specialists in the computer science field of "artificial intelligence," although we admit we cannot offer a precise definition of this field. People interested in pattern recognition and, to a lesser extent, self-organizing systems, may find parallels to their work here. Similarly, our theoretical models and simulation studies are relevant to psychological work on the simulation of human learning and problem solving. Psychologists working on human information processing will, hopefully, be able to benefit from the book. Finally, the computing techniques used can be considered as alternatives to conventional statistical techniques (especially multivariate discrimination analysis) in some situations. As such, they should be of interest to anyone who is attempting to discover a classification rule, in any field.

While the primary value of this book will probably be as a research report, it has been written in a form suitable for use as supplementary reading in seminar courses on artificial intelligence, pattern recognition, human learning, and complex mental processes. An effort has been made to keep the book self-contained so that it can be so used without additional references.

As with any joint work, the authors have split their task. The research has been primarily under Hunt's direction. The work was carried out at the University of California, Los Angeles, from 1961 to 1963, and at the University of Sydney, Australia, from 1963 to 1965. Hunt was responsible for the initial preparation of the entire manuscript. The research reported in Chapters 6 and 7, and the final form of those chapters, resulted from collaborative efforts by Hunt and Marin. Similarly, the application of concept-learning techniques to text analysis, reported in the first part of Chapter 8, was a joint effort by Hunt and Stone. Marin and Stone read and commented upon the entirety of the next-to-last draft. This differed significantly from the final version only in that it did not include discussion of the Algol programs (CLS-9, reported in Chapter 5) or the discussion of medical data-processing work reported in Chapter 8.

Naturally, many people have helped us at different stages of our work. We wish to mention a few who, although in no way responsible for our errors, gave us many helpful comments which improved the text considerably. Dr. Christopher Wallace (Sydney), Dr. James MacQueen (UCLA), and Dr. Walter Reitman (University of Michigan) read and commented upon the entire manuscript. Professor Jacob Marschak of UCLA clarified and contributed to our discussion of the decision problems involved in choosing between artificial intelligence systems on the basis of experimental evidence. Mrs. D. Crawford (Sydney) and Miss Jaroslava Krivanek (University of California, Irvine) were of great assistance in the preparation and editing of the various drafts, and in addition read various sections for comment and discussed some of the experiments with me. They improved both the clarity and the content of the report. This sort of work would be impossible without the active support of the computing centers involved, which had to put up with a great deal of non-standard, non-system computing. Professor George Brown of UCLA, then Director of the Western Data Processing Center, and Professor John Bennett of Sydney, Director of the Basser Computing Centre, were personally of great assistance in seeing that we did, indeed, receive excellent support. Our thanks also to the staffs of the two computing centers.

From 1961 until 1963 this work was supported by a Ford Foundation grant to the Western Management Science Institute, UCLA. The work at Sydney was supported by a United States Public Health Service grant. This financial assistance is gratefully acknowledged.

Finally, on behalf of myself and my coauthors, I should like to thank the secretarial and administrative staff who have prepared the reports, programs, diagrams, and manuscripts which have been involved. The willing and resourceful efforts of Mrs. Edna Vincent and Miss Pat Wheatley at Sydney, and Mrs. R. Nelson at UCLA, managed to override my own tendencies toward disorganization enough to complete the report in a finite time.

EARL HUNT

January, 1966

Contents

PREFACE v

SECTION I   PURPOSE AND FORMAL MODEL

Chapter 1. Plan of Research

1. Introductory Remarks 3
2. Concept Learning Problems 7
3. Notation 14
4. Concepts as Sequential Decisions 16
5. Notation for Trees 18
6. Computation 20

Chapter 2. Formats for Concept Learners

1. Generalized Concept Learners 25
2. Notation for Describing Concept Learning Systems 29
3. Concept Learning Problems 32
4. Problem Sets 35

SECTION II   EXPERIMENTS IN ARTIFICIAL INTELLIGENCE

Chapter 3. Concept Learning System 1. Basic Results

1. Description of the Program 45
2. Experiment I 51
3. Experiment II 58
4. Experiment III 64
5. Discussion 67

Chapter 4. The Effect of Restricted Memory

1. Limited Memory Systems 71
2. Experiment IV 72
3. Experiment V 77
4. Experiment VI 80
5. Comment on Limited Memory Systems 83

Chapter 5. Changes within CLS Heuristics

1. Selective Sampling 87
2. Experiment VII 90

3. Alternate Subproblem Selection Techniques 93
4. Problem Redefinition 97
5. Experiment VIII 97
6. Application of a Decision Criterion to Experiment VIII 99
7. CLS-9. An Attempt to Combine Effects 107
8. Discussion of the Artificial Intelligence Experiments 113

SECTION III   SIMULATING HUMAN CONCEPT LEARNING

Chapter 6.   Simulating Human Concept Learning.
Learning the Logical Connectives

1. Simulating Human Concept Learning 119
2. The Material 120
3. Experiment X 123
4. Experiment XI 127
5. Experiment XII 130
6. Relation to Other Psychological Studies 133

Chapter 7.   The Random Categorization Task

1. Responding to Random Categorization 139
2. Experiment XIII 140
3. Discussion 146

SECTION IV   APPLICATIONS AND DISCUSSIONS

Chapter 8.   Applications of CLS Programs

1. The Content Analysis Problem 151
2. The General Inquirer System 153
3. California Money Bills: An Example from Politics 159
4. Suicide Notes: A Psychiatric Example 164
5. Future Biographies: An Example from Social Anthropology 165
6. Some Anticipated Developments in Automatic Content Analysis . . . 168
7. Application to Medical Statistics 170

Chapter 9.   The CLS in the Context of Other Research

1. The General Pattern Recognition Problem 175
2. The Feature Word Experiments 180
3. The Work of Uhr and Vossler 186
4. Relation to All-or-None Concept Learning 188
5. The EPAM Model of Verbal Learning 190
6. Evaluation of CLS's 193

Appendix A. Computations in CLS Programs

1. Notation and Conventions 197
2. Special Definitions Used in Discussing Concept Learning 200
3. Programs 201

Appendix B. Summaries of Statistical Tests,
Experiments IV, V, and VI

1. Experiment IV 223
2. Experiment V 225
3. Experiment VI 227

Appendix C. An Algol Program Defining CLS-9

1. Introduction 229
2. Program 230

References 239

AUTHOR INDEX 243

SUBJECT INDEX 245

Experiments in Induction

Section I

Purpose and Formal Model

CHAPTER 1

Plan of Research

1. INTRODUCTORY REMARKS

This is a report on the nature of a thought process. Our studies have not been limited by the traditional boundaries of psychology, philosophy, or mathematics.

It may appear that we claim to have produced a thesis to be compared with Locke's *On Human Understanding*. We have not; our work has been far more prosaic. We have studied just one facet of intelligence, concept learning, and that only in a restricted situation. Still, the work has been "problem oriented" rather than "discipline oriented." We have tried to find out something about the nature of concept learning without concerning ourselves too much with the question of how what we were finding out fitted into the current theories in the several fields on which we touched.

An intelligent device, including man, can be thought of as something capable of adjusting to its environment. To make such adjustments the device must continually be classifying slightly different states of the environment as equivalent or not equivalent. The particular classifications may vary from time to time: sometimes we group whales with bears; sometimes we group whales with sharks. Still, the intelligent device must classify. Now suppose that we wish to design such a device. Unless we, the designers, know all the states of the environment which the device may encounter, we have no way of prewiring it with the appropriate classification rules. Instead we must provide it with a capacity to develop classification rules from experience. We shall refer to such development as *concept learning*, and a device that can perform this act will be called a *concept learning system*, or, for short, *CLS*.[1]

We shall report what happened when we built a mechanical concept learning system. By "built" we mean that we wrote a digital computer program which directed a machine to perform manipulations on symbols. That the machine we used was a high-speed digital computer is, at least

---

[1] We regretfully join the ranks of those who speak of LISP, COMIT, IPL-V and, for that matter, USN, USA, UK, USPHS, ONR, and all the other acronyms. In some contexts "concept learning system" is simply too clumsy to say.

logically, not important. The original motivation for designing a CLS was to construct a simulation of human behavior. Before doing this, however, some time was spent studying the effects of changes in various parameters both of the system and of the types of problems presented to it. We found that there were interesting aspects of the computer program's performance which seemed worth reporting without regard to whether or not they mirrored aspects of human performance. At the same time, we remained interested in the question of whether or not the machine could simulate human performance. Thus we became interested in the design of both simulations of human behavior and artificial intelligence systems.

There is no necessary connection between these two problems. Minsky (1961) and Neisser (1963), among others, have presented a convincing argument that the discovery of a good artificial intelligence device might tell us nothing at all about human problem solving, and that knowing all about human problem solving might not help us a bit in designing artificial intelligence systems. But again, it might. One should not prejudge the issue either way. There is no necessary contradiction in running two programs diverging from the same basic theme. This is what we have done. Others seem to have done the same thing. It has never been clear to us whether the motivation for Newell, Shaw, and Simon's pioneering work on the development of computational techniques for symbol manipulation (Newell et al., 1955, 1958, 1959; Newell and Simon, 1957, 1961a) was research in psychology or in computing methods. We do not think the distinction is important. Certainly the resulting ideas and research, of which this monograph is one contribution, have affected both fields. That such a result was not certain beforehand does not mean that it could not happen.

Given, for the moment, our claim that we can build a concept learner, what should we try to show about it? As a first step, we can show that if a particular environment is assumed, the CLS under investigation either is or is not capable of developing concepts to order that environment. Similarly, we may force subjects in a psychological experiment to operate within the same abstract setting. We can then compare the performance of the CLS with that of a human concept learner. Such studies lie in the fields of artificial intelligence and the psychology of learning. At some point we have to ask, "What are the important environments?" The answer to this question is bound to be a value judgement, and can only rest on the evaluation of case studies. We shall report one application in some detail. In it the programs used to simulate human concept learning and to solve abstract problems in inductive logic were used as part of a system for automated analysis of the content of English text. In a second study, which we shall not take up in detail, related programs were applied to a problem in medical diagnosis.

This monograph is written for at least three disparate audiences: psychologists, designers of artificial intelligence devices, and people interested in the application of pattern recognition techniques to complex problems. In this section we introduce the basic ideas, terminology, and notation which will be used throughout the report. The second section discusses experiments with different CLS programs as artificial intelligence devices operating in an abstract environment. The third section reports some experiments comparing CLS performance with the performance of university students in concept learning experiments. In the fourth section a description is given of how the CLS technique is being used in the practical problem just mentioned, and some comparisons are made between our techniques and alternative approaches.

Throughout, we shall be referring to the actions of computer programs. How should we describe these actions? There are several possibilities: we could present a verbal description, show flow diagrams of varying detail, describe the programs in some specialized notation, or present the actual programs which were used. The alternatives are listed in order of specificity, from least to most, and in order of readability, from most to least. Presenting verbal descriptions suffers from the problem that words are never adequately defined, so a misunderstanding might arise which would be crucial if someone attempted to replicate our work. Flow diagrams, unless they are carried to the point of unreadability, often suffer from the same ambiguity. On the other hand, a specific computer program involves a great deal of "housekeeping" computations, such as arranging for proper printing of results, ensuring that the core storage of the particular machine being used has not been exceeded, and the like. Leaving these computations in would result in our reporting a program "readable" by only a very few programmers with experience with the particular computer system we used, removing them bodily would result in our reporting a program that would not run. We have chosen a compromise. In the text we describe the program verbally, resorting to simple flow diagrams where these are felt to help the explanation. In Appendix A the programs stating the logic of every operation are recorded using Iverson's (1962) notation for describing computation. The decision to use Iverson's notation was made after receiving varied comments on this point from viewers of an earlier draft. The three authors themselves are not in agreement, each preferring a different alternative, so that the solution adopted was imposed by E.B.H. in his role as first author. The only other reasonable alternatives seemed to be Algol (Naur *et al.*, 1960) or Information Processing Language V (IPL-V) (Newell, 1964), the language actually used in most of the computer programming. The IPL-V programs, however, contained a great many housekeeping subroutines of the type just described. In addition, IPL-V pro-

grams are difficult for the nonspecialist to follow and the language itself
is somewhat "exotic" in the sense that it is not available for all commonly
used machines or taught by all computing departments.

An earlier draft of this report contained descriptions of the computations
used in an extension of Algol, the international programming language.
Since Algol was originally defined by rigorous adherence to syntactic definition, the task of extending the language is, itself, not to be taken lightly.
Since Algol was not designed with the sort of computation with which we
are dealing in mind, full definition of a CLS requires so many programming
tricks that the programs become virtually unreadable. In addition, it
would be necessary to use the full power of the defined language, rather
than the actual power available to users of existing Algol systems. (This
problem is the familiar one in computing: practically every operating system represents a method of translating a subset of the language to be used,
rather than the entire language.) In order to present a compromise which
would be useful to others, we do present a modified CLS which, for many
purposes, is as good as the complete systems we describe, which can be
defined in terms of an operating Algol system. This program is presented
in Appendix C. The compiler used to run the program has been described
in detail by Randall and Russell (1964). Therefore, it should be possible
for the interested programmer to reproduce much of our work within the
framework of compiler systems available on most computers.

However, as we have noted, Algol is not a satisfactory vehicle for describing the complete CLS. To do this we have gone to a second machine-
independent language, that defined by Iverson. The Iverson language is
extensively documented in an easily available reference, and contains as
primitive terms many of the operations used in CLS programs. This makes
it possible to describe CLS programs clearly and concisely. To aid in doing
this, a brief statement of Iverson's notation is given in Appendix A.

Appendices A and C are intended primarily as a guide to those who wish
to reproduce our work. Every attempt has been made to make the text
intelligible without reference to the appendices.

The research we are reporting is not complete. Most of our results are
suggestive rather than final. There were several reasons for reporting now,
one of them being administrative convenience. Our main reason, however,
is that we feel that our experience may prove useful to others. The computing methods we have developed and used appear to have wide applicability. Our techniques for evaluating our efforts seem to be sufficiently
different from those in use in psychology and computation to be worth some
comment in themselves. Thus the work can be regarded as an example of
the way to evaluate simulations and artificial intelligence systems as well
as a report of the workings of a particular program.

2. CONCEPT LEARNING PROBLEMS

We need a formal language for describing the task of identifying, sorting, and classifying objects. Since an intuitive justification of the notation we propose and an elaborate description of the way it can be used are available elsewhere (Hunt, 1962) the notation system will be presented without detailed consideration of other alternatives.[2,3]

DEFINITIONS

2.1 *Objects* are the entities which may be observed by a concept learner. The set of all objects is the *universe*, **U**.

2.2 Objects can be distinguished, one from the other, by the value they have on certain *attributes*. Thus an attribute is a dimension of variation of an object.

2.3 The *description* of an object is a statement of its position on all observable attributes.

2.4 A *value* is a set of those positions of an attribute which are to be treated equivalently.

2.5 A *description space* is the set of all possible descriptions of objects. Since an object can have at most one position on a given attribute (and, hence, have only one value) the description space is the set of statements formed by combining one value from each attribute.

Definitions 2.1–2.5 provide our basic frame of reference.

It is useful to state these definitions in a mathematical notation, both to ensure precision and to lay the basis for the logic of the computer programs which we have used.

The ith attribute, in some arbitrary numbering scheme, may be represented by a vector $\mathbf{a}^i$ whose components are symbols indicating possible values of that attribute. Thus "size" could be represented by the vector (large, medium, small). Although in this example the order of values in the vector corresponds to an ordering along a physical dimension this will not, in general, be the case. If we had an attribute "girls' names," represented by (Mary, Alice, Jane), the ordering would clearly be arbitrary. No generality is lost if we use numbers to indicate the values of attributes. It would be irrelevant (to a computer) if the attribute "girls' names" were to be rewritten (1, 2, 3). In the next few examples both numerical and verbal representations will be given. In later examples, however, the reader

---

[2] Similar notation systems have been proposed by Banerji (1962) and Restle (1961).

[3] The notation system which we use is a slight modification of that proposed by Iverson. A complete description is set forth in Appendix A, Section 1.

should remember that in a computer any natural language word may be replaced by a number. Arithmetical operations are then meaningless, but we can still operate using identity and nonidentity.

An attribute-value scheme will be represented by a matrix which summarizes all possible descriptions. Let this matrix be $\mathbf{A}$, in which each of the columns represents a single attribute. Entry $\mathbf{A}_{ij}$ of the matrix will be the ith value of the jth attribute. Since the ordering of values within an attribute is arbitrary the rows of $\mathbf{A}$, which represent a particular value of each attribute, are meaningless. If this scheme were to be applied blindly, we should find that some columns of $\mathbf{A}$ were longer than others, since there is no rule that states that all attributes must have the same number of values. By appending null elements (to be indicated by the symbol $\bigcirc$) to the attributes with fewer values until all attributes are represented by column vectors of the same length, this difficulty can be overcome.

At this point it is convenient to introduce some additional notation for matrices in general. Let $\mathbf{M}$ be any matrix. The row dimension of $\mathbf{M}$ is defined as the number of elements in a row, hence the number of columns. Similarly, the column dimension is defined as the number of rows, or the length of any column. The vector corresponding to the ith row of $\mathbf{M}$ will be denoted by $\mathbf{M}_{i\cdot}$. Similarly, the jth column will be denoted by $\mathbf{M}_{\cdot j}$. A vector, when treated separately, will always be treated as a row vector.

Following Iverson, we shall use $v(\mathbf{M})$ and $u(\mathbf{M})$ for row and column dimension, respectively. At times, $v(\mathbf{M}_{i\cdot})$ may be used for the dimension of a vector.

Table 1.1 gives an example of the notation and of the attribute-value scheme. This example will be used in clarifying some further points in this chapter.

The description of an object is the set of values which that object has on its attributes. Suppose $\mathbf{d}$ is the description of an object. Then $\mathbf{d}_j$ will be the value which that object has on attribute j. This implies that $\mathbf{d}_j$ is one of the nonnull symbols of $\mathbf{A}_{\cdot j}$, i.e. that it is a permissible value of attribute j. While this scheme is a generally applicable one, it does not provide for three important cases. Two of these are handled by further conventions, the third will be ignored.

The value of a particular object on some attribute may be unknown. For instance, we might know the size and type of an animal but not its color. In this case the corresponding element of the vector describing the animal will be replaced by $\bigcirc$. Thus if all we knew about an animal was that it was a large bear it could be described within the system set forth in Table 1.1 by the vector (large, $\bigcirc$, bear). In the numerical coding (Table 1.1c) this would be written (3, $\bigcirc$, 1).

Although the second and third cases will not arise in our artificially con-

TABLE 1.1
EXAMPLE OF ATTRIBUTE-VALUE SCHEME AND NOTATION

(a) Original Attributes and Values

Size = (small, medium, large)   Attribute 1
Color = (black, brown)   Attribute 2
Type = (bear, dog, cat, horse)   Attribute 3

(b) Attributes Expanded into Vectors with Common Dimension,
$$v(\mathbf{A}_{.1}) = v(\mathbf{A}_{.2}) = v(\mathbf{A}_{.3}) = 4$$

$\mathbf{A}_{.1} = $ (small, medium, large, O)
$\mathbf{A}_{.2} = $ (black, brown, O, O)
$\mathbf{A}_{.3} = $ (bear, dog, cat, horse)

(c) Attribute-Value Scheme Using Coded Symbols; Matrix Dimensions,
$$v(\mathbf{A}) = 3, \; u(\mathbf{A}) = 4$$

$$\mathbf{A} = \begin{pmatrix} 1 & 1 & 1 \\ 2 & 2 & 2 \\ 3 & O & 3 \\ O & O & 4 \end{pmatrix}$$

---

trived situations they are of sufficient interest for us to indicate how they might be handled. One can think of attribute-value systems in which not all attributes are applicable to all objects being described. A good example is the U.S. government's practice of having the same medical questionnaire for both sexes. In this case a second, noninteger symbol (say, #) may be used in the jth position in a description to indicate that the jth attribute is meaningless for the object being described.

There is a third exceptional situation in which the formal description may violate our common sense notions of how objects ought to be described. In the formal system an object may have only one value on a given attribute. In natural language we often use attributes which do not have mutually exclusive values. Saying that a Chevrolet is the sort of car that a man can drive does not imply that a woman cannot drive one. Another example actually arose in our work on text analysis. Stone *et al.* (1962) have found that it is sometimes useful to describe sentences by locating the syntactical position of classes of words in the sentences. For instance, the sentence

Our army pledged allegiance to the flag

could be described by locating "violence" and "patriotism" terms in it. Patriotism terms, however, appear in the subject, verb, object, and indirect object. Thus if "position of patriotism terms" is to be an attribute in our formal description system, the formal method is inadequate. This can be avoided by defining the set of possible values of this attribute as the set of combinations of one or more syntactical positions. While this avoids the conceptual problem, it may create a formidable practical problem if computations are to be based on the now expanded description space. In practice, we were able to avoid this sort of situation in our experimental work and we shall not treat it further.

Every object in the universe will have a description attached to it. There may be more than one object with the same description; by the same token there may be no objects with a given description. Thus any description or partial description defines a (possibly empty) set of objects.

We now require some further definitions. These, which are largely adopted from Church (1958), relate more directly to concept learning.

FURTHER DEFINITIONS

2.6 A *name* is an arbitrary label attached to every object in a particular subset of the universe. The name has a *denotation* and a *concept*.

2.7 A *denotation* of a name is the set of objects to which the name can be applied.

2.8 A *concept* is a decision rule which, when applied to the description of an object, specifies whether or not a name can be applied.

2.9 A *concept learning system* (CLS) is a device for creating a concept corresponding to some partition of a sample of objects which have been categorized by a pre-established rule for using a name. It is assumed that the CLS forms its concept by observing examples of the use of a name, i.e., by observing a subset of objects in the universe and being informed of whether or not the name is applicable to them.

In an experiment an experimenter decides upon a concept and uses it to state which descriptions are of positive or negative instances. A CLS is then shown a sample of objects, with class membership stated. The CLS attempts to find a concept which will categorize all objects in the universe in the same manner as the experimenter has categorized them. This is the concept learning problem, as it has been studied extensively both in psychology (where the CLS is almost always a human being) and in the development of artificial intelligence systems. As recent reviews of the literature are available (Hunt, 1962; Sebesteyen, 1962; Uhr, 1963) no attempt will be made to discuss the work done by others except where it is directly relevant to our own research.

It should be noted that the concept learning problem is a variant of what Sebesteyen (1962, p. 4) has called the pattern detection and recognition problem: "[the] common objective is to recognize membership in classes, where classes are known to us only through a set of their samples." The pattern recognition problem is more general, however, since it is possible that two objects with exactly the same description will be members of different classes. In this case only probabilistic decision making rules can be used. We specifically ruled out the study of such situations in our original statement of the problem. In any practical CLS some policy for handling such cases must be formulated.

The CLS can never be certain that it has obtained the correct concept unless it has seen at least one example of every possible description. This is because the experimenter could always use a general rule with arbitrary exceptions which the learner would have no way of guessing. In the context of the example given in Table 1.1, we could define the class of "dangerous animals" to be "all large animals except large, black horses." If a learner was never shown a large, black horse why should he think this subset of objects would not follow the more general rule that large animals were dangerous? In particular, why should large, black horses be any different from large, black bears or large, brown horses, both of which differ from the exception only in the value of one attribute, and both of which are, by definition, dangerous?

But surely this is too perverse a situation. Granted that an experimenter, in a laboratory setting, could behave in any way that he liked, would this be an analog to any real life concept learning situation? Probably not.

Fortified by the reasonableness of this argument, and motivated even more by a desire to define a solvable concept learning problem, our research has been conducted in a more restricted situation. Hovland (1952) pointed out that if the logical form of the correct concept is stated, so that the learner need only fill in the relevant attributes and values, then the concept may be defined without explicit knowledge of the class membership of objects of every conceivable description. Hunt (1962, p. 33) has extended this argument somewhat further, showing that the logical form need not be completely defined: only the number of relevant characteristics (i.e., attributes and values) need be stated. Kochen (1961a) has provided a similar argument. All three of the discussions rest on the same basic ideas. If the number of relevant attributes are specified in advance, then one could write down in a "memory bank" all the possible concepts which could exist, before ever being shown a single example. Each of the concepts would establish an assignment of every object in the universe to either positive or negative instances. Now suppose there were c possible concepts, with an assignment corresponding to each. Every time an example is shown all the learner has to do is to check his list of possible assignments and cross off from a list of possible answers any concepts whose assignments are not in agreement with the observed class membership of the example. Eventually, when there is only one concept remaining, the problem will be solved.

In practice, the "memory for possible answers" model is not feasible. Unless the problem is very simple the size of memory required to write down the assignments, and the amount of processing needed, would be too much for the largest computing system imaginable. This is because the number of possible concepts grows in something very similar to a "super-exponential" function as the number of attributes increases. (For justification of this claim, see Kochen, 1961a.) However, there are algorithms[4] which, by assuming that the complete logical form of the concept is known (e.g., the answer will be of the form, "Either value w of attribute x or value y of attribute z," with x, w, y, and z not specified in advance) can lead to the discovery of a solution. Algorithms for solving conjunctive problems are given by Bruner et al. (1956) and by Kochen. Bruner et al. and Kochen (1961b) also give algorithms for solving disjunctive problems. None of these algorithms make impossible requirements on either memory or computation speed. Kochen's disjunctive problem solving techniques also do not require that the exact logical form of the concept be known in advance. However, his techniques do assume that all attributes have only two values. While any description scheme can be recast in binary form, this complicates the representation of the problem (cf. Hunt, 1962, p. 257).

We are not going to deal further with these algorithms because it appears to us that, with the exception just noted, the situation they presuppose is as unrealistic as the situation in which arbitrary exceptions are allowed. The learner must know some highly esoteric information, the exact logical form of the concept. Imagine a medical research worker who would be willing to use a scheme for discovering a diagnostic procedure that worked only if the desired procedure was guaranteed, in advance, to involve just three tests, all of which had to be satisfied for a particular diagnosis to be made. If the physician knew this much about the problem at the beginning, he would almost certainly also know what the three tests were and there would be no problem. We are not saying that it is not sometimes useful, for the purpose of psychological experimentation, to place this restriction

---

[4] For those not familiar with the term, we shall use *algorithm* to mean a rule for computing a function of specified values. Thus "applying algorithm x to A" does not mean that a correct function of A has been computed, but merely that certain precisely defined calculations on A have been performed.

The definitions and conventions we use are intended to apply only to the restricted concept learning situations we have studied, and not to concept learning situations in general. Thus our language is a specialization of the more general terminology proposed by Hunt (1962), and may deviate from his terminology slightly in order to handle more effectively our particular problems.

on the situation. However, we have investigated a more general situation.

In succeeding chapters we shall consider the performance of a class of CLS's with the following properties:

(a)   When presented with a sample of the universe, the CLS's provide a concept that can be used to classify the entire universe without performing an undue amount of computation on the sample. In other words, the CLS's we consider must be pragmatically realizable.

(b)   The concepts returned by the CLS's *tend* to be as simple ones as can be used to classify the sample. It is as if the learner assumed that the true concept did not contain arbitrary, unstated exceptions.

(c)   The methods will be valid and will obtain the correct answer, if shown enough information, regardless of the true form of the concept. (Some exceptions to this will be noted in certain cases.)

When we think of concept learning in this way, we see at once that it is a hierarchal affair. One must have a concept in order to learn more concepts. Any value of an attribute is itself a concept. For example, at one level the value "red" of the attribute "color" may be thought of as a defining attribute of the concept "fire engine." At another level "red" is clearly a label which can be applied to any member of a set of objects: fire engines, apples, and lipsticks. Thus, we must have the concept of "red." It is clear, then, that when we speak of concept learning devices we are talking about devices which discover rules for combining previously learned concepts to form a new decision rule. At some point we must assume that the concept learner has some previously learned concepts, since these are needed to establish the description space. We shall have nothing at all to say about how these primitive constructs might be formed, by either a machine or a human being.

This characterization of concept learners will, by definition, rule out many other forms of concept learning, for example, probabilistic discrimination and the learning of relational concepts. We do this not because we feel that such learning is unimportant, or that it is not what one might want to include within the term "concept learning," but simply to make clear the class of learners we are investigating in this particular study. There is no claim that the devices we shall study are representative of all possible devices capable of complex learning. We merely claim that our CLS programs are included within the set of learning devices, and represent an interesting subclass within that set.

Finally, we wish to avoid controversy on another semiphilosophical point. Is the attribute-value notation sufficient to represent all problems involving what one would normally call "conception"? Certainly "red" can be thought of as a concept, and cast within the attribute-value notation.

But what about the still more primitive concept of color itself? More generally, cannot one think about attributes, as well as values, as being more primitive concepts than the concepts defined in a particular description space? And if so, can the attributes be defined by a description space notation? Intuitively, it is harder to see how such a formalization applies to the "set of objects to which the attribute 'color' applies" than to "the set of objects which have the color red." Philosophically the question is interesting. Pragmatically, we can avoid it. We shall deal with the learning of concepts which can be represented within the attribute-value notation. Clearly, nontrivial concepts of this type exist. An attribute-value notation converts quite naturally to a matrix notation, as we shall show in Section III, and this provides a useful guide to computation. There is no claim that either the attribute-value notation or the isomorphic matrix representation is the only or even the most general notation possible. It has proven a useful technique in our work, and for our purpose this is sufficient justification.

3. NOTATION

If there are n attributes in an attribute-value scheme, the scheme itself may be summarized by a matrix $\mathbf{A}$ of row dimension n and column dimension m, where m is the maximum number of values appearing in any attribute. There may be null entries in $\mathbf{A}$. An object may be described by a vector $\mathbf{d}$, of dimension n, in which some of the elements might be the special symbols $\bigcirc$ (value unknown) or $\#$ (inapplicable). We shall generally disregard the latter two cases. Given the description of an object we will want to indicate whether it is a positive or negative instance. This can be done by appending to the description vector, as the $(n + 1)$st symbol, the numeral one if the instance is positive, zero otherwise. Now consider the matrix $\mathbf{D}$ whose rows, $\mathbf{D}_{i.}$, each represent a distinct description. This matrix is of row dimension $n + 1$ and column dimension k, where k is the number of possible different complete descriptions. $\mathbf{D}$ satisfies the following statements:

3.1 $\mathbf{D}_{ij} \neq \bigcirc$ for all i, j (no null elements).

3.2 $\mathbf{D}_{ij} \in \mathbf{A}_{.j}$ for all i, j. Any symbol $\mathbf{D}_{ij}$ which appears in column j of row i defines the value of attribute j on object i, and hence must appear in column j and some row of matrix $\mathbf{A}$, which defines the attribute-value scheme.

3.3 $\mathbf{D}_{i,n+1} \in \{0, 1\}$ for all i.

One way to state a concept is to specify the matrix $\mathbf{D}$ since the $(n + 1)$st column of $\mathbf{D}$ assigns each possible description, and hence each possible object, to the class of positive or negative instances. This will be called the *full form* of a concept.

Another, more economic, way to state a concept involves the use of partial descriptions. Again, the ideas introduced previously must be extended slightly. Recall that a partial description involved the specification of the values of some attributes. Obviously, there is a set of complete descriptions which satisfies any given partial description. If we are given a set of r partial descriptions, each of which is satisfied only by objects within a given class, then these partial descriptions can be used to state the concept, simply by forming them into a matrix of size $n + 1$ by r, and using the $(n + 1)$st column to indicate the class membership of the objects described by each row. Sufficient partial descriptions must be given to provide at least one partial description of each object in the universe.

It is often useful to extend the idea of partial descriptions to include specification of what the value of a particular attribute is *not*. This can be indicated by a negation sign, $-$, placed in front of the appropriate element. Thus if we are given an attribute-value scheme **A** and a concept stated as a matrix **C** whose rows are partial descriptions plus classification indicators, then

3.4 $$\mathbf{C}_{ij} = -\mathbf{A}_{kj}$$

indicates that all objects satisfying partial description i do not have the kth value of attribute j. For example, using the symbols of Table 1.1 we could say that if all large, black animals that were not horses were dangerous, this could be translated as

3.5 $$\mathbf{C}_{i\cdot} = (\text{large, black}, -\text{horse, 1})$$

or, using the numerical coding scheme of Tables 1.1b and 1.1c,

3.6 $$\mathbf{C}_{i\cdot} = (1, 1, -3, 1).$$

The partial description technique leads to a much briefer statement of concepts than the statement in full form. Suppose we wanted to state that, "All large animals and all bears are dangerous." In logical terminology dangerous animals are "large or bear." This concept can be expressed in full form by stating 24 different descriptions and their class membership, as indicated in Table 1.2. The same concept can be stated by the three partial descriptions shown in Table 1.3. This could be cut even further if we adopted the convention that partial descriptions are used only to describe positive instances.

When a concept is stated by specifying a set of partial descriptions the statement will be called the *partial form* statement of the concept. For every

TABLE 1.2
Full Form Statement of Concept, "Bears or Large Animals
Are Dangerous"[a]

	Attribute 1	Attribute 2	Attribute 3	Class
	Small	Black	Bears	Dangerous
	Medium	Black	Bears	Dangerous
	. .	. .	. . .	. . .
	Large	Brown	Dogs	Dangerous
D =	Small	Black	Cats	Not dangerous
	. .	. .	. .	. . .
	Medium	Black	Horse	Not dangerous
	Large	Black	Horse	Dangerous
	. .	. .	. .	. . .
	Large	Brown	Horse	Dangerous

[a] Words, rather than symbols, are used for readability.

concept there is just one full form but there may be several equivalent partial forms.

TABLE 1.3
Partial Form Statement of Concept Shown in Table 1.2[a]

	Attribute 1	Attribute 2	Attribute 3	Class
	Large	*	*	Dangerous
C =	*	*	Bear	Dangerous
	−Large	*	−Bear	Not dangerous

[a] The symbol * indicates that the object description may have any allowable value.

4. CONCEPTS AS SEQUENTIAL DECISIONS

Although concepts can be defined by stating a set of descriptions, it is often more convenient to represent a concept as a sequence of tests of the values of individual attributes. To illustrate by example, suppose that all persons who apply for driver's licenses can be described by the attributes sex (male, female), age (young, adult, mature, old), criminal status (no record, record of misdemeanor, felon), and driving skill (passed test, failed test). The rule for assigning the label "legal driver" is, "Any person who is not a felon and who has passed the driver's test is a legal driver," which defines the concept of legal driver as

(male, young adult, no record, passed test)
(male, young adult, misdemeanor, passed test)
⋮
(female, old, misdemeanor, passed test),

excepting only those descriptions which contain the characteristic (i.e., value of an attribute) "felon" or "failed test." It is much easier to represent this concept as a sequential decision rule. To decide whether any person is eligible for a driver's license one first asks, "Has he (she) passed the driver's examination?" and then, "Has he committed a felony?" If the answer to the first question is "no," or the second "yes," then the person is not eligible.

It is easy to think of such rules as sequences of questions. These will be called *decision trees*. Formally, they are directed graphs showing the various possible sequences of questions, answers, and classifications. A decision tree for the driver eligibility example is shown in Fig. 1.1. All the decision

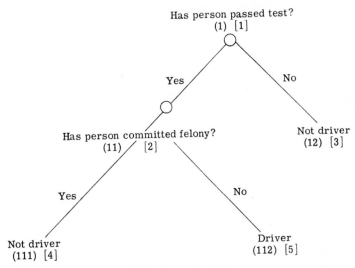

Fig. 1.1. A tree of sequential decisions for classifying applicants for driving licenses. The index of each node is indicated in parentheses. The serial is indicated in brackets.

trees we shall discuss begin at their highest point, or *node*. Perversely, this is called the root of the tree. From each node there are exactly two lines extending downward to two lower nodes. Associated with each node is a set of values of attributes. If an object being classified includes in its description all the characteristics named at a particular node the object is passed to the node to the lower left. Otherwise the object is passed to the node to the lower right. At some point an endpoint or *leaf* will be encountered. A leaf is a node with no nodes below it. Associated with each leaf is a set of objects—those objects whose descriptions contain the combination of characteristics required to reach that leaf. Thus any object will have a path through the tree. If objects routed to a particular leaf are positive (negative) instances, the leaf will be called a positive (negative) endpoint.

A given partial description may be realized by several equivalent trees. One faces the problem of stating which of several logically equivalent trees are, in some sense, "best." There are different criteria which can be used; they do not always lead to the same answer.

The reason for having a concept is to classify. Classification, in turn, implies that an object be passed through a decision tree in the cheapest manner possible. The economic term is used purposely; it is often useful to think of the act of testing an attribute as having a cost. So, too, it is often useful to think of correct and incorrect classifications as having a certain worth. For instance, in medical diagnosis some of the attributes of a patient may be specified by cursory examination; others may require such heroic measures as exploratory operation before they can have their values stated. Obviously, classification rules based on cheap tests are to be preferred to classification rules based on expensive tests. However, the matter is not quite that simple. Minimizing the average cost implies that both the cost of testing and the frequency with which objects of different descriptions are encountered are known. To choose the cheapest decision tree the concept learner must know the relative frequencies with which each path of a tree will be used after the concept is formed.

Another characteristic which may be used to choose between different decision tree representations of a concept is simplicity. It is easier to understand the actions of a tree with few nodes than to understand the actions of a tree with many nodes. This, of course, must be weighed against the cost of using the tree and the accuracy of the tree. However, it is not a small consideration. If 90% of the objects in the universe can be classified by a very simple tree, while classifying the remaining 10% requires an elaborate tree, there is something to be said for using only the simpler concept.

Finally, we must consider not only the cost of using a classification rule, or the cost of understanding it, but also the cost of acquiring the rule. In the following chapters we shall show that different techniques for developing a sequential decision tree vary widely in the amount of computation required on the same data. Thus the resulting decision rule can be thought of as an item with high or low production cost. Even if the concept is not a perfect classifier of all objects in the universe, its low cost of production may more than make up for its inaccuracies.

5. NOTATION FOR TREES

In this section a matrix notation for describing sequential decision trees will be developed. The techniques used are a special case of Iverson's method of filial-heir chains (Iverson, 1962, p. 127).

Every node in a tree is assigned an index number by successive application of the following rules:

5.1 *The root of a tree has index 1.*

5.2 *If the index of a given node is* i, *the node to the lower left has index* $10i + 1$ *and the node to the lower right has index* $10i + 2$.

The nodes are then ranked in ascending order of their index numbers. Serial number j is assigned to the jth node in this ranking. Thus the root always has serial 1, the node to the lower left of the root serial 2, the node to the lower right serial 3, and so on. The node with serial j will be called the jth *node*.

Figure 1.1 shows the index number and serial number of each node in a decision tree.

A tree will be represented by a matrix $\mathbf{T}$ in which each row, $\mathbf{T}_{j.}$, represents the jth node of the tree. As usual, the tree will be stated with reference to an attribute-value system depicted by an n by m matrix $\mathbf{A}$. If there are s nodes in the tree, $\mathbf{T}$ will be a matrix of row dimension $n + 2$ and column dimension s in which the elements are defined as follows:

5.3. *If the ith node is not a leaf, element* $\mathbf{T}_{ij}$, $1 < j < n$, *is either null or is a possible value of attribute j.*

5.4 *If the ith node is not a leaf, element* $\mathbf{T}_{i,n+1}$ *is the serial number of the node to the lower left of node i. Element* $\mathbf{T}_{i,n+2}$ *is the serial number of the node to the lower right of the ith node.*

5.5 *If the ith node is a leaf, element* $\mathbf{T}_{i,1}$ *is 1 if all objects routed to this leaf are positive instances, zero if they are all negative instances. All other elements of* $\mathbf{T}_{i.}$ *are zero.*

The use of a tree matrix for classification can be stated simply. Initially set i equal to one, thus starting at the root of the tree. The classification procedure is defined by the action at any root, i (alternatively, any row of $\mathbf{T}$).

5.6 *Examine* $\mathbf{T}_{i,2}$. *If it is zero a leaf has been reached and the appropriate classification is established by* $\mathbf{T}_{i,1}$. *If it is not zero apply rule 5.7:*

5.7 *Compare the description of the object being classified and the first n elements of* $\mathbf{T}_{i.}$. *If the nonnull elements of* $\mathbf{T}_{i.}$ *are each equal to the corresponding elements in the description, d (i.e.,* $\mathbf{T}_{ij} = \mathbf{d}_j \neq \bigcirc$ *for all $j < n$), set i equal to* $\mathbf{T}_{i,n+1}$ *and then repeat step 5.6; otherwise set i equal to* $\mathbf{T}_{i,n+2}$ *and repeat 5.6.*

An example of a decision tree to represent the concept "dangerous animals are large or are bears" is shown in Fig. 1.2. Its associated matrix $\mathbf{T}$ is shown in Table 1.4. When a concept is represented by a directed graph or by a matrix $\mathbf{T}$ it will be said to be in *tree form*.

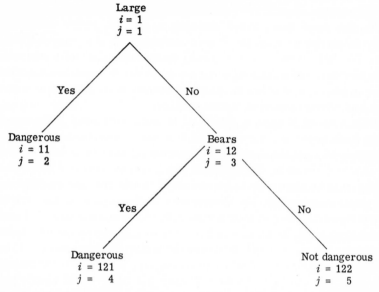

FIG. 1.2. Graph of concept "dangerous animals are large or bears." Indices (i) and serials (j) for each node are shown.

A program showing the step-by-step analysis specified by rules 5.6 and 5.7 is given in Appendix A, Section 3.

TABLE 1.4
MATRIX FORM OF CONCEPT SHOWN IN FIG. 1.3[a]

		Column 1	Column 2	Column 3	Column 4	Column 5
Row 1	Large	○	○	2	3
Row 2	Dangerous	0	0	0	0
Row 3	○	○	Bear	4	5
Row 4	Dangerous	0	0	0	0
Row 5	Not dangerous	0	0	0	0

[a] Words have been used instead of symbols to increase readability.

6. COMPUTATION

The idea of computing a concept does not fit as well with normal English usage as it might. Still, it is central to our research and must be explained. Given a sample containing both positive and negative instances, a concept learner must decide what concept was used to classify both the sample and the universe from which it was drawn. There will, as we have pointed out, be several possible concepts unless the sample contains representatives of every point in the description space. Within some limitation on computing effort, the concept learner must choose one of the possible concepts and must, at the same time, avoid choosing a concept which could not correctly categorize at least the known sample. This is a computational problem. We shall attempt to show this by statement and a verbal example. To show how the problem of computing a concept can be set up as a machine program, however, it is sufficient (but not necessary) to indicate how the problem can be represented in matrix notation.

Consider a set of N objects, drawn at random from some well-defined universe. Each object will have a description and a classification. As indicated previously, the description and classification may be indicated by a vector of $n + 1$ elements, the first n of which specify values of attributes (including inapplicability or indeterminacy), using the last element to indicate class membership. The descriptions of the objects in the sample may be grouped together to form a matrix $\mathbf{S}$, of row dimension $n + 1$ and column dimension N, in which row $\mathbf{S}_i$. is the description of the ith object in the sample. It is possible for two rows to be identical but, unless one of the rows contains the null symbol as one of its first n elements, two rows cannot differ in only the $(n + 1)$st element. If they did, they would violate the rule that two objects with identical descriptions must belong to the same class.

A "computation" can be thought of as any sequence of arithmetical or logical operations which operates on a symbol or set of symbols to produce another symbol or set of symbols. Thus a computer program is a computation. Using this idea, a special *concept learning computation* may be defined.

6.1 *A concept learning computation is a computation which operates on a matrix of the form of matrix* $\mathbf{S}$, *to produce a decision tree.*

Inside a computer a tree would be represented either in matrix form or in some equivalent representation, such as a list structure (Newell, 1964). This is a programming detail which will be ignored. Trees will be represented in text in either graphic or matrix form as convenient.

At times it is convenient to distinguish between samples and trees available to a CLS at two different times t and t'. These will be distinguished by a superscript, i.e., $\mathbf{S}^t$ is the sample available to the CLS at time t. Time will be viewed as discrete, one unit of time passing whenever the available sample is altered in any way, including transformation to an identical sample if that is one of several alternative transformations.

To illustrate, we offer a simple computation. This particular concept learning computation is one of those proposed by Bruner *et al.* (1956) as algorithms for solving conjunctive concept learning problems (in which all positive instances contain in their descriptions a set of specified values of attributes) without using excessive memory capacity. The algorithm, which they call the *wholist strategy*, is doubly interesting because it will figure in our work and because it appears to be one of those strategies adopted by intelligent human concept learners in the experimental situation of Bruner *et al*.

The algorithm is simply stated. Take as the first trial hypothesis the set of all attributes and values present on the first positive instance. Call this the *focus*. Compare the focus with the set of attributes of values present on the next positive instance and set the focus equal to the intersection of the two. Repeat this on each positive instance, in succession, until all positive instances have been examined. The resulting focus can be used as a test to define the class membership of any object.

This algorithm works as stated if one can assume that the answer is a conjunctive one. If a check is desired, the focus can be compared with the description of each negative instance. All elements of the focus should never be found within such descriptions. If they are, the assumption of a conjunctive answer is incorrect and the algorithm cannot work. There is no need to have any more information present at one time than the focus and the description of the object currently being examined.

A detailed program realizing the wholist strategy is presented in Appendix A, Section 3. The sequence of computations to be executed on a matrix is obvious from the description. All that is needed is a successive scan along the rows of S, ignoring any row in which the $(n + 1)$st (last) entry is zero. The *focus* is defined as a vector which is initially set equal to the first n elements of the first row of S in which the $(n + 1)$st entry is one, and modified by having the appropriate elements set equal to the null symbol whenever variation in a given attribute is detected on subsequent testing of positive instances. The result will be a vector containing all nulls (if there is no answer) or a vector in which the nonnull elements indicate a test to be executed at the only nonleaf node in the corresponding tree.

The computation is simpler to do than to describe. An example is offered in Table 1.5. The reader can verify, if he wishes, that the resulting focus

TABLE 1.5

SAMPLE MATRIX FOR DEFINING CONCEPT "DANGEROUS ANIMALS
ARE LARGE AND BEARS"[a]

$$
S = \begin{pmatrix}
\text{Large} & \text{Brown} & \text{Bear} & \text{Dangerous} \\
\text{Small} & \text{Black} & \text{Horse} & \text{Not dangerous} \\
\text{Large} & \text{Brown} & \text{Dog} & \text{Not dangerous} \\
\text{Large} & \text{Black} & \text{Bear} & \text{Dangerous} \\
\text{Medium} & \text{Brown} & \text{Bear} & \text{Not dangerous}
\end{pmatrix}
$$

[a] Words have been used in place of symbols for readability.

vector defines the concept, "All dangerous animals are *large and bears*," as shown in the tree of Fig. 1.3.

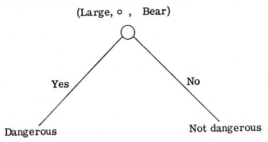

FIG. 1.3. Tree corresponding to concept defined by Table 1.5 using wholist algorithm.

CHAPTER 2

Formats for Concept Learners

1. GENERALIZED CONCEPT LEARNERS

Concept learning is a type of inductive reasoning. Perforce, the steps necessary in inductive reasoning must also be necessary in concept learning. Polya (1954), in discussing induction in mathematics, defined the following steps.

(1) Evaluate the available evidence to form a conjecture. The conjecture must be adequate to account for what is known and should "probably" be true when tested against new evidence.

(2) Get some new evidence.

(3) Test the conjecture against the new evidence. If the conjecture is proven false, re-evaluate the total evidence now available to find a new conjecture.

Evaluate, in the concept learning situation, implies that there is some record available to the learner of what he already knows. There is a huge volume of literature on information storage and retrieval, and an equally huge volume on human memory; its very existence suggests that arranging such a record is not a trivial task. Clearly one does not evaluate all the information ever presented; one evaluates the information available at the time that the question is asked. Similar questions could be asked about Polya's steps for forming conjectures, selecting new evidence, and testing a conjecture. We shall try to relate these questions, first to the general ideas about concept learning presented in Chapter 1, then to a particular concept learning system.

A CLS must have a (perhaps imperfect) memory for information presented to it. By examining the information in its memory, the system has to be able to provide, in full, partial, or tree form, a trial concept or *hypothesis.* Since the information in memory may be regarded as a sample, the computation which evaluates memory is a concept learning computation. The system must also have some way of evaluating the concept against fresh evidence. The act of obtaining this evidence will be called selection, and a computation which specifies the evidence to be obtained will be called a selection computation.

These computations can be fitted together in several ways. Any particular scheme for specifying how they interact can be thought of as a plan for a generalized concept learning system. A specific CLS is then stated by indicating what the actual algorithms are for selection, transfer from selection to memory, evaluation of new evidence, and concept computation. We will be concerned with two types of generalized CLS's, *independent* and *interactive* selection systems.

First, we deal with the independent system. Here concept learning proceeds by the following steps:

(1) A sample of objects is selected from the universe by some random device. The sample is arbitrarily ordered.

(2) The first item in the sample is transferred to the memory section of the concept learner.

(3) The learner uses the information now in memory to compute a trial concept.

(4) The next item in the sample is transferred to memory.

(5) The trial concept is used to classify the new item. If the classification was correct, the system returns to step (4), unless there are no more objects in the sample. If the classification was incorrect and if there are more objects in the sample, the system returns to step (3).

(6) The experiment stops when there are no more objects in the sample.

The procedure is shown graphically in Fig. 2.1. The distinguishing feature of an independent selection system is that the order in which information is shown to the learner is independent of the concepts the learner develops. Thus if we had two concept learning programs, either of which could be fitted into box 4 of Fig. 2.1, which program was used would make no difference whatsoever in determining the information that would flow between boxes 1 and 2.

The *interactive selection* system does not have this property. Consider the following change in the procedure just specified. Instead of invariably picking the next object, in order, from the sample for transfer to memory, do this only when classifications are correct. When classifications are incorrect examine the sample to determine,by some test, what object in the sample is likely to be "informative" in the sense that it provides a good test of the new hypothesis. (Recall that since the classification was incorrect, a new hypothesis must have just been computed.) Then select this object as the next instance to be transferred from memory. This procedure is outlined in Fig. 2.2.

The basic difference between the two systems is that in the second system

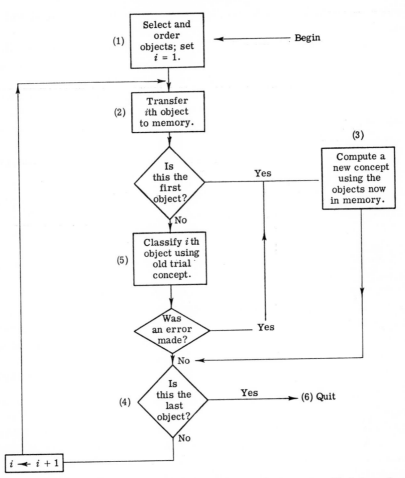

Fig. 2.1. Flow diagram for generalized concept learning system with independent selection.

it is not possible to write down, in advance of the experiment, what the order of selection of objects is going to be. How concepts are computed makes a difference to this order in interactive selection systems, whereas it did not in independent selection. The effect is to provide a sort of "feedback control," since the interactive selection system has the capacity to monitor its own output.

We have not exhausted the possible variations of control we could put into a generalized concept learning system. For instance, we have not considered systems in which the CLS develops a new concept not only by evaluating the information in memory but also by evaluating its previous

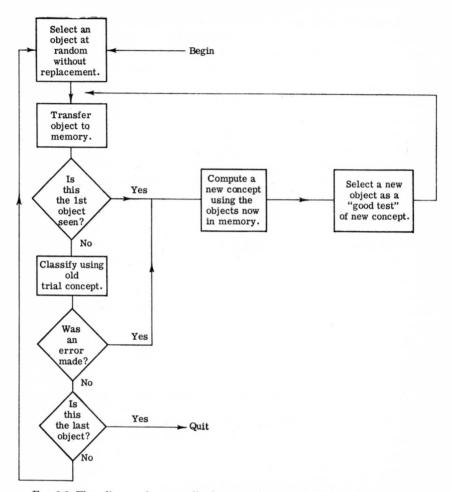

FIG. 2.2. Flow diagram for generalized concept learner with interactive selection.

hypothesis. Specific CLS's of the two types just described did seem interesting because there is a suggestive analogy between the differences between systems and the differences between certain "real life" concept learning situations. The selection-independent system is, in some ways, an analogy to induction based on correlational studies of uncontrolled observations. Consider the astronomer, who must form his ideas of the galaxy by observing events whose occurrence he cannot arrange. He can be contrasted to the physicist who, by use of suitable equipment, can arrange for situations which would never occur in the ordinary course of events (e.g., the reactions in a linear accelerator) but which, if they can be made to occur, will probably provide him with a good test of his current ideas. The experimental scientist must decide what a good experiment is, and he will not always be right in his decision. On the other hand, experimenters are right often enough to warrant the hope that an effective selection-interaction CLS using completely automated selection rules could be developed. The analogy should not be carred too far, since a real life example is bound to be imperfect. For example, astronomers have the option of deciding what to look at, and we appear to be approaching an era in which astronomical experiments will be possible. The general idea remains valid.

One would expect that the systems capable of more complex selection would be better concept learners. On intuitive grounds this is reasonable. At a logical level, Bruner *et al.* (1956) described several strategies for constructing what might be called an "information rich" sequence of examples when the concept learner had control over selection. They also showed that college students would, in psychological experiments, use this control to construct these sequences. A direct comparison between independent and interactive selection conditions in human subjects has shown that there is an advantage to human beings in interactive selection which is not just related to the presence of information in memory; the human learner must also be "ready to use it" in some sense that, at present, is not fully understood (Hunt, 1964b).

But we are getting somewhat ahead of ourselves. We must next indicate, in somewhat greater detail, the type of computations which we shall describe and how they can be set up as computer programs.

2. NOTATION FOR DESCRIBING CONCEPT LEARNING SYSTEMS

Assume that an attribute-value scheme has been established and is specified by a matrix $\mathbf{A}$ of row dimension n and column dimension m, as defined in Chapter 1. An example, which uses the attributes size (big, little), character (lazy, thrifty, bad), and animal (pig, wolf) is shown in Table 2.1. This will be used in subsequent illustrations.

TABLE 2.1
ATTRIBUTE-VALUE SCHEME USED IN ILLUSTRATIONS

	Attribute 1 (size)	Attribute 2 (character)	Attribute 3 (type)
$\mathbf{A} = $	Big Little O	Thrifty Lazy Bad	Pig Wolf O

Having established $\mathbf{A}$ we may specify a concept in full form by a matrix $\mathbf{D}$ of row dimension $n + 1$ and column dimension p. As before, the last column of $\mathbf{A}$ states which rows are descriptions of positive and negative instances. It will be assumed that there is one and only one object which can be described by each row of **D**. Thus selecting an object is equivalent to stating a row of **D**. Table 2.2 shows the **D** matrix associated with the example of Table 2.1.

TABLE 2.2
FULL FORM OF CONCEPT "BIG, OR THRIFTY ANIMALS ARE VIABLE"

	Attribute 1	Attribute 2	Attribute 3	Class
	Big	Thrifty	Pig	Viable
	Big	Lazy	Pig	Viable
	Big	Bad	Pig	Viable
	Big	Thrifty	Wolf	Viable
	Big	Lazy	Wolf	Viable
D =	Big	Bad	Wolf	Viable
	Little	Thrifty	Pig	Viable
	Little	Lazy	Pig	Not viable
	Little	Bad	Pig	Not viable
	Little	Thrifty	Wolf	Viable
	Little	Lazy	Wolf	Not viable
	Little	Bad	Wolf	Not viable

Let **S** be the sample matrix, in which each row is identical with a row in **D**. **S** will be of row dimension $n + 1$ and of column dimension N, where $N < p$.

Initially, we shall assume that the rows of **S** are chosen by random sampling, without replacement, from the rows of **D**. Thus if we think of a vector, $\mathbf{j} = \{j_i\}$ of N different integers, each element of $\mathbf{j}$ having been chosen by independent random sampling without replacement from the set of integers 1, 2,..., p, **S** is defined by

2.1 $$\mathbf{S}_{i\cdot} = \mathbf{D}_{j_i\cdot}.$$

For example, if in the example of Tables 2.1 and 2.2 we define j by

2.2 $$j = (1, 7, 9),$$

then Table 2.3 specifies the sample to be used.

TABLE 2.3
SAMPLE CHOSEN BY SAMPLING VECTOR (1,7,9) FROM
DESCRIPTION SPACE STATED IN TABLE 2.2

	Big	Thrifty	Pig	Viable
S =	Little	Thrifty	Pig	Viable
	Little	Bad	Pig	Not viable

If the number of items in the sample, N, is equal to p, the number of possible descriptions, then S will be a random rearrangement of the rows of D.

In dealing with interactive selection systems this scheme breaks down, since the idea of a prespecified sample is inappropriate. Fortunately, a fairly straightforward modification of the notation permits us to specify S appropriately. Discussion of this problem will be postponed until the problem of selective interaction is taken up in detail in Chapter 5.

Memory will always be used in a very restricted sense, to refer to a matrix, M, whose rows are descriptions of the objects whose classifications are known to the learner at some point t. Thus, by definition, the rows of M are identical with those rows of S which have been designated as available to the learner, so any computation defined for a sample matrix may be performed on a memory matrix.

Only two alternate definitions of memory systems will be considered, *expandable* and *fixed storage* systems. The computational details are given in Appendix A, so a verbal description is sufficient here.

One can think of an expandable memory as one in which the concept learner has an infinitely long row of boxes, each of which can hold exactly one description. Every time a new object appears, its description is stored in the first empty box in the row. While this is not a practical system for any realistic problem, and is certainly not realistic psychologically, it is a useful situation to investigate as a limiting case. A fixed size system is somewhat more realistic, since the learner has a finite number of boxes. The number of boxes will normally be less than the number of descriptions in the sample, so that the learner can never consider the entire sample at once. When a new object appears its description is stored in a randomly chosen box, any previous contents the box may have had being dumped out.

By way of illustration of how simple the ideas discussed are, Table 2.4 continues the example of Tables 2.1–2.3, showing successive states of an expandable and fixed size memory.

Many information retrieval systems (libraries, for instance), use specific areas of memory space to store certain types of items. In some of the experiments to be reported a start has been made on amplifying memory in this way by using two small memory systems, $+M$ and $-M$, within the general scheme of a fixed size memory. The storage rules are exactly the same as those just given, except that only positive instances have their descriptions stored in $+M$, and only negative instances in $-M$. The result is that in the complete memory available to the concept learner, the union of these two small matrices, the relative frequencies of positive and negative instances will be determined by the relative sizes of the two small matrices as well as by the frequency of positive and negative instances in the sample.

TABLE 2.4
POSSIBLE EXPANSION OF FIXED AND VARIABLE MEMORIES FROM
SAMPLE IN TABLE 2.3

Time	$\mathbf{M}^t$ (expandable)	$\mathbf{M}^t$ (fixed size)	$K(t)$
$t = 0$	(Empty)	$\begin{pmatrix} \circ & \circ & \circ & \circ \\ \circ & \circ & \circ & \circ \end{pmatrix}$ (Empty)	
$t = 1$	(Big, Thrifty, Pig, Viable)	$\begin{pmatrix} \circ & \circ & \circ & \circ \\ \text{Big} & \text{Thrifty} & \text{Pig} & \text{Viable} \end{pmatrix}$	2
$t = 2$	Big, Thrifty, Pig, Viable Little, Thrifty, Pig, Viable	$\begin{pmatrix} \circ & \circ & \circ & \circ \\ \text{Little} & \text{Thrifty} & \text{Pig} & \text{Viable} \end{pmatrix}$	2
$t = 3$	Big, Thrifty, Pig, Viable Little, Thrifty, Pig, Viable Little, Bad, Pig, Not viable	$\begin{pmatrix} \text{Little} & \text{Bad} & \text{Pig} & \text{Not viable} \\ \text{Little} & \text{Thrifty} & \text{Pig} & \text{Viable} \end{pmatrix}$	1

We now turn to the evaluation computation. In Chapter 1, Section 5, the procedure for classifying a description was stated (5.6, 5.7). Given a description and a tree form of a concept, the description was passed to an endpoint and then classified as a positive (negative) instance depending on whether it reached a positive (negative) endpoint. An appropriate program is outlined in Appendix A, Section 3. The classification will be said to be correct if the description passed to the endpoint at time t (i.e., the description specified by S_t.) is, in fact, of a positive (negative) instance.

The only thing that remains is to state how a concept learning computation is to be specified in the notation system. To do this an added, quite important, definition is required.

2.3 *A concept learning computation is a series of operations on a memory matrix which produces a concept stated in tree form.*

Thus a concept learning computation can be written

2.4 $$f_i(\mathbf{M}^t) = \mathbf{T}^t$$

to indicate the application of the ith type of concept learning function to a memory matrix as it exists at time t, producing a tree form concept as the trial concept at time t.

3. CONCEPT LEARNING PROBLEMS

All the experiments which we shall report in Sections II and III followed the same general paradigm. First a concept was selected. This was always written down first in tree form. The CLS being investigated was then presented with examples of positive and negative instances. When appropriate, this selection was done in interaction with the CLS involved. The dependent variables recorded to describe CLS performance were the number of erroneous classifications made before computing the current concept, the number of items in the sample which were presented before the correct concept was computed, and in some cases, a measure of the amount of computation required.

A very large number of concepts could be defined. In fact, if there are N possible descriptions there are 2^N possible concepts. In selecting concepts to be learned some sort of systematic variation of correct answers had to be carried out. This variation took the form of systematic changes in the structure of the tree form of the concept. It turned out to be one of the most important determinants of CLS performance, so we now describe the criteria for choosing concept learning problems in some detail.

To do this, some additional definitions are needed. The first is the notion of relevance. Let $\mathbf{T}^*$ be a tree form of the concept chosen as "correct" by the experimenter. The value of an attribute (*characteristic*, for short) is *relevant* if it appears as a test at some node in $\mathbf{T}^*$. For instance, in the example of a concept of legal drivers (Chapter 1) the relevant characteristics are "felon" and "passed driver's test," since questions about each of these characteristics must be asked in order to decide if a person is a legal driver. Similarly, if one of the values of an attribute is a relevant characteristic, then the attribute will be called a *relevant attribute*. Continuing the example, the relevant attributes of the concept "legal driver" are "criminal status" and "driving skill."

A concept can be described by its *content* and its *structure*. The term *content* will be used to refer to the exact questions which the concept specifies. The term *structure* will be used to refer to the arrangement of nodes and endpoints relative to each other in the tree form of the concept.

3.1 Content: *Two concepts are identical in content if they have the same relevant characteristics.*

This definition groups together two concepts which may represent different distinctions based on the same information. For instance, consider the alternate definitions offered by Bruner *et al.* (1956) of a "citizen of Altavista."

(a) "A citizen is a resident of Altavista *or* a property owner in the town."

(b) "A citizen is a resident of Altavista *and* a property owner in the town."

These two definitions have identical content, since one needs to know the same things about a person to decide whether or not he is a citizen. On the other hand, the two concepts apply citizenship to different people.

3.2 Form: *Two concepts are identical in structure if, for every relevant attribute in the first concept, and for every value of that attribute, there is a one-to-one transformation into the set of relevant attributes and values of the second concept such that if the attributes and values in the first concept are replaced by their transforms the second concept is produced.*

By definition 3.2 two concepts which are identical in form have an identical arrangement of nodes and endpoints, regardless of the questions asked at each node. In addition, if a particular characteristic is questioned at one or more arbitrarily chosen nodes in one decision tree, then its corresponding characteristic must be questioned at the same node in the decision tree of the other concept.

The idea of equivalence of structure is illustrated by the following alteration of the example "citizen of Altavista."

(a) "A citizen of Altavista is a resident or a taxpayer."
(b) "A citizen of Altavista is a knave or a fool."

Both examples are identical in structure but not in content. Now note a third example:

(c) "A black card is a club or a diamond."

This concept is not identical with (a) or (b) in content or structure. The misidentity with content is obvious. The misidentity with structure arises because the same attribute (suit) is interrogated at both nodes of (c), whereas different attributes (location of residence, location of owned property or moral status, mental status) are queried in (a) and (b).

3.3 Restricted interest: *We shall be interested only in changes in concept learning due to choice of concepts of a different structure.*

This restriction permits us to study concept learning "in the abstract" by directing our attention to the information processing characteristics of the problem's structure rather than its content.

The restriction is clearly an aid in the study of artificial intelligence devices per se. It is something of a disadvantage when we wish either to simulate human concept learning or to apply a particular concept learning strategy in a concrete situation. There is more than ample evidence to show that human concept learning is affected by variables which are relevant to a person's perception of a given situation, as well as by the manner in which the relevant variables combine to form a concept. In simulating human concept learning we shall have to partial out such effects by appropriate experimental controls. This has the effect of removing an important variable in human performance from our simulation. The only excuse we can offer for doing so is that we believe that an adequate understanding of why human beings focus on particular variables in a concept learning situation cannot be developed until a complete theory of perception is offered. Until such time, we shall have to be content with the simulation of a limited sphere of human activity.

3.4 Single tests of attributes: *Only a single question will be asked about any one attribute. This question will take the form, "Does attribute* $A_{.j}$ *have value* A_{ij}?*" The identical question may be repeated at different points in the tree, but no further questions concerning* $A_{.j}$ *can be included.*

In other words, if attribute $A_{.j}$ is relevant all that need be known about that attribute is whether or not it has value A_{ij}. This restriction is introduced solely to simplify the problems with which we shall deal.

3.5 Description: *All objects will be described by both relevant and irrelevant attributes. The latter are attributes which do not contain any characteristics questioned at any point in the correct concept.*

A good CLS is one which locates quickly the attributes which are relevant to the concept being learned, thus minimizing the number of tests to be made when an object is classified.

4. PROBLEM SETS

Each of the experiments reported in Sections II and III involves the application of one or more CLS's to each problem within a set of problems of varying complexity. Three such sets of problems were considered. They represent still further restrictions of our experimental situation. However, it is simply impossible to study all the possible problems that one could think of, or that could be generated by some algorithm for providing new combinations of positive and negative instances. Hopefully, our criteria for choosing problems did lead to interesting choices. In any case, our criteria can be, and are, stated explicitly.

PROBLEM SET I

The description space was defined by assuming four attributes, each with four possible values. Attributes $A_{.1}$ and $A_{.2}$ were always relevant, with values A_{11} and A_{22} the crucial values. The set itself consisted of the five problems shown in Fig. 2.3.

These particular concepts were thought to be interesting for both logical and historical reasons. The five trees shown correspond to the five most

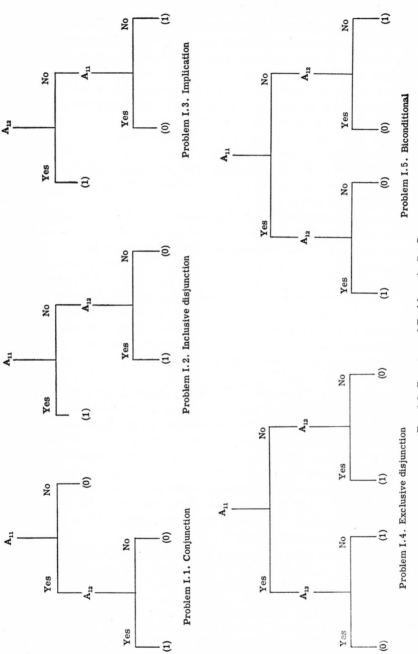

Problem I.1. Conjunction

Problem I.2. Inclusive disjunction

Problem I.3. Implication

Problem I.4. Exclusive disjunction

Problem I.5. Biconditional

Fig. 2.3. Structure of Problems in Set I.

frequently used (of 16 possible) binary relations between two variables. Problem I.1 is a conjunctive problem; positive instances are defined as those objects which can be described as having both characteristics A_{11} and A_{12}. Problem I.2 is an inclusive disjunctive problem; positive instances have either characteristic or both of them. In problem I.3 all positive instances have characteristic A_{12} or do *not* have characteristic A_{11}. Another way of saying this is to state that the presence of A_{11} implies the presence of A_{12}. In problem I.4 all positive instances have one or the other characteristic but not both, an example of an exclusive disjunctive relation. Finally, in problem I.5, either all positive instances have *both* characteristics or they have *neither* characteristic. The two characteristics stand in a biconditional, or "double implication," relation: the presence of one implies the presence of the other.

These five relations have figured prominently in the history of symbolic logic. "Implication" and "biconditional" ("if and only if") are basic to the syllogism, a form of logical argument dating back at least to Socrates. The two disjunctions and conjunction were introduced in formal logic later, although they are more primitive relations. (*Implication* and *biconditional* can be defined in terms of conjunction and disjunction.) This is a bit hard to believe, at first, since the operations *and* and *or* seem to be so basic to language itself. The disbelieving reader is asked whether the statement "John and James can defeat Thomas" means that either John or James can exhibit mastery, or whether it means that they must gang up on Tom (Lewis and Langford, 1932).

It might be argued that even if the historical importance of a question is granted, further justification is needed for spending time and money on it today. Four of the five relations are still used in the development of logic in modern texts (e.g., Suppes, 1960). Exclusive disjunction seems to have dropped out of logic, but concepts involving exclusive disjunction can arise in practical cases. Dobzhansky (1962) describes an example. In certain parts of Central Africa viable individuals must have one of two alleles of a gene, but not both.[1] Since the five concepts in Problem Set I seem to be important "in the world," the effect they have upon concept learning should also be interesting.

If the problems are interesting, why are they interesting here? The other

[1] The example is a case of "hybrid vigor." An individual who is heterozygous for a particular gene pair is more fit for survival than either of the two possible homozygotes. In the case in question, there is a gene pair, *si*, *Si*, such that if an individual has both recessive alleles (genotype *si si*) he will probably die of sickle cell anemia before reaching adolescence. However, individuals who have only one recessive allele (genotype *si Si*) are resistant to malaria. Since malaria is endemic in the tropical regions in which the gene is found, these heterozygotes are more likely to survive (Dobzhansky, 1962, pp. 150–154).

reasons for studying them are self-contained in the framework of our research effort. The five problems differ in their form in interesting ways. As Fig. 2.3 shows, there are three trees with two test nodes and two trees with three test nodes. If multiple tests are allowed at one node (as they are in the definition of tree forms in Chapter 1, Sections 4 and 5), problem I.1 can be represented by a single node.

In addition, we can use these problems to study the effect of negation. Problem I.4 is the negation of I.5: positive instances of one are negative

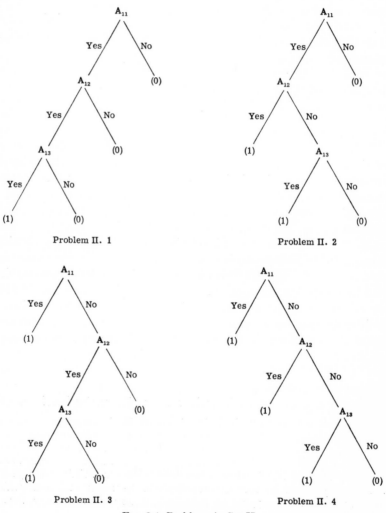

Fig. 2.4. Problems in Set II.

instances of the other. To a perfect concept learner this should make no difference, it should be as easy to define the complement of a class as to define the class itself. However, it is harder for people to define negations than to define classes, since they prefer to extract their information from positive instances. [See Hunt (1962) for a review of the considerable amount of research available on this point. Two experiments by Wason (1960, 1961) are particularly relevant.] Evidently people make the heuristic assumption that names are not arbitrary, that objects within a class have more in common with each other than do objects outside of the class. This is reasonable, when we think of how names are used. If one did not know what a marsupial was, and were to be presented with some examples of animals that were marsupials and some examples of animals that were not, a reasonable initial assumption would be that the concept "marsupial" was based on some properties found in most marsupials, and that "not marsupials" referrred to a heterogeneous lot of animals. We shall return to this point in the next section.

Problem Set II

Set II contained four problems of greater complexity of form than the five problems in Set I. The tree forms are shown in Fig. 2.4. Each concept contained three relevant dimensions, $A_{.1}$, $A_{.2}$, $A_{.3}$. As in Problem Set I, the first value was relevant, defining the set of relevant characteristics (A_{11}, A_{12}, A_{13}). The four problems were created by concatenating the three relevant dimensions and two connectives, conjunction and inclusive disjunction, in the following manner: First, the three relevant dimensions were partitioned into the sets ($A_{.1}$) and ($A_{.2}$, $A_{.3}$). Two groups of problems were created by combining these two sets by either conjunction or disjunction. Then, within the second set, the two relevant dimensions were related to each other by either conjunction or disjunction. The resulting statement was used as a statement of the characteristics defining positive instances as follows:

Problem II.1, positive instances described by $A_{11} \cdot (A_{12} \cdot A_{13})$;
Problem II.2, positive instances described by $A_{11} \cdot (A_{12} \lor A_{13})$;
Problem II.3, positive instances described by $A_{11} \lor (A_{12} \cdot A_{13})$,
Problem II.4, positive instances described by $A_{11} \lor (A_{12} \lor A_{13})$.

In addition to the three relevant attributes, the objects used in Problem Set II were described by four irrelevant attributes, each with four values. Thus the problems represented an increase in both relevant and irrelevant complexity over the problems in Set I.

PROBLEM SET III

Problem Set III represented a further increase in complexity. The four concepts used in this set are shown in Fig. 2.5. To form a problem for this set the four relevant dimensions were partitioned into the sets $\{\mathbf{A}_{.1}, \mathbf{A}_{.2}\}$, $\{\mathbf{A}_{13}, \mathbf{A}_{14}\}$. The two sets were combined by either conjunction or disjunction, and the two dimensions within a set were similarly combined. Because

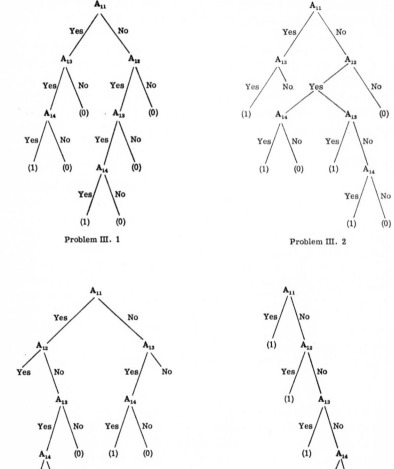

FIG. 2.5. Problems in Set III.

of the large amount of computer time required to complete experiments with this set, not all possible problems were used. A selection was made to give an idea of the effects of introducing conjunctions and disjunctions at various levels. Thus in problem III.1 the positive instances are those having characteristics $(\mathbf{A}_{11} \vee \mathbf{A}_{12}) \cdot (\mathbf{A}_{13} \cdot \mathbf{A}_{14})$.

As in Set II, the objects categorized in Problem Set III were described by four irrelevant attributes, each with four values, in addition to the relevant attributes. Thus Problem Set III required concept learning based on a fairly complex eight-variable description space.

Experiments in Artificial Intelligence

CHAPTER 3

Concept Learning System 1.   Basic Results[1]

1. DESCRIPTION OF THE PROGRAM

This and the following two chapters describe specific CLS programs which fit into the general framework presented above. To evaluate the different programs we conducted experiments in which the different CLS's were used to solve the problems of Problem Sets I, II, and III. The rationale for using these problems has already been presented, and if it is accepted, then the experiments can be thought of as interesting abstract problems. We have tried to choose a wide enough variety of problems so that we were not open to the charge that we tailored the programs to solve the particular problems on which they were tested.

Occasionally we shall refer to "real world" problems, such as might be faced by a physicist, astronomer, or physician, which have some resemblance to our experimental work. In fact, we have already made some such references. These analogies, which are intentionally loose ones, are intended only as pedagogical devices. Hopefully they will aid the reader (particularly if he is a casual reader) in following our line of reasoning. The examples and analogies do illustrate the sort of thing which we hope artificial intelligence programs will do, someday, and they may aid anyone who wants to understand why we did what we did. The illustrations are not intended to be statements, or even suggestions, that we have constructed a device which could replace highly skilled human concept learners. Neither are the illustrations intended to show that we have produced a computer program which solves concept learning problems in the way that human beings do. *Neither claim can be made solely on the basis of artificial intelligence experiments.* To substantiate a claim that a program is a model of human performance it is necessary to make very explicit comparisons between the

---

[1] Portions of this chapter have appeared previously as Western Management Science Institute working paper No. 6, "The development of decision trees in concept learning: Model and Basic Results," by Earl Hunt, available from The Western Management Science Institute, U.C.L.A. A presentation of some of the results of Experiments I and II was made at The Institute for Management Science-Operations Research Society of America meetings in San Diego in 1962.

human and artificial subject. We shall, in later chapters, present some data addressed to this point, but we are not developing a model of human learning here. The way to substantiate a claim that a computer program can replace a human concept learner is also clear: one offers case studies. We do not have such examples in the next three chapters.

The first CLS studied, CLS-1, was a program quite similar to the one proposed by Hunt and Hovland (1961) as a model of human concept formulation. This program provided the starting point for our later work, since it was progressively modified into a more sophisticated system. We shall begin by describing the results obtained with the original program, and then illustrate the effect of the changes made in it.

The selection and memory subroutines of CLS-1 were perhaps its greatest simplifications. Objects were selected for inclusion in the sample by the random procedure defined in Chapter 2, Section 2, in which the rows of the sample matrix, **S,** are determined by random selection, without replacement, from the rows of the matrix **D** of possible descriptions of objects. The "perfect infinitely expandable" memory defined by equation 2.3 in Chapter 2 was also used, i.e., once an item was in memory it remained there *in toto*. At any point t $(t < N)$, the first t of the randomly chosen descriptions were available for inspection by the program.

The learning method used in CLS-1 computation is an algorithm in the sense that it always will produce some answer that is sufficient to classify the sample (but not necessarily the universe from which it was drawn) into positive and negative instances. The computation is heuristic in the sense that it contains "rules of thumb" which will usually produce a structurally simple tree form of a concept, with a minimum of computation. A program specifying CLS-1 computations is given in Appendix A, Section 3. The basic ideas can be grasped by considering the key steps in the computation and by following an example.

The CLS-1 computation routine can be thought of as an attempt to apply the wholist algorithm (defined in Chapter 1, Section 6) to a problem or to a concatenation of subproblems derived from it. The computation begins with a sample of objects to be classified. In order, the following things are done:

(1) A search is made for some characteristic (value of attribute) or set of characteristics which appear in the description of all positive instances and never appear in the description of any negative instance. If such a characteristic or set of characteristics is found, it is made the test associated with the root of the concept in tree form; the point to the lower left of the root is a positive endpoint, and the point to the lower right a negative endpoint. The problem is then solved.

(2)   If the procedure in step (1) cannot be carried out, it is reversed. A search is made for a set of characteristics which appear in the descriptions of all negative and no positive endpoints. If such a characteristic or set of characteristics can be found, then the problem is solved as before, except that the positive and negative endpoints are reversed.

The simplicity of the computations in steps (1) and (2) should be appreciated. Assuming that the information in memory is stored in matrix form, all that the CLS need do is to compare successive rows representing positive (negative) instances, column by column. At the first comparison all columns are compared. At the second comparison, only those columns which were identical in the first and second descriptions are compared, and so on. If the learner runs out of columns at any point the method is known to have failed.

Since it is possible that both steps (1) and (2) will fail, a further step is needed to allow for nonconjunctive concepts:

(3)   If steps (1) and (2) fail, count the frequency with which characteristics appear in the description of *positive instances only*. Choose this characteristic as the test at the node.

(4)   Split the sample of objects available for examination into two subsamples, one containing all objects which have the characteristic just chosen, and one containing all objects that do not. In general, both positive and negative instances may be in either or both subsamples. Set up two new concept learning problems based on each of these subsamples. The first node of the tree of the problem based on the subsample of objects containing the characteristic is the node of the lower left of the current node; the first node of the tree based on the other subsample is the node to the lower right.

(5)   Solve the subproblem to the lower left. (This may require setting up sub-subproblems.) Then solve the subproblem to the lower right.

This procedure implicitly assumes that there are both positive and negative instances in the original sample. If at any point in solving either the original problem or a subproblem the CLS encounters a sample or subsample containing only positive (negative) instances, the current node is immediately made a positive (negative) endpoint and the next subproblem attacked.

In steps (1) and (2), if a set of characteristics is suggested as a test, the sample is also examined to see if any one of these characteristics alone would also be a sufficient test for splitting the positive and negative instances. If it is, then the single characteristic is chosen as the test at that node. When more than one characteristic qualifies for selection as a test, a random choice between qualifying characteristics is made.

To illustrate, let us follow through an example. Consider the universe of all possible four-letter "words" made up only of consonants. These can be described by four attributes: first letter, second letter, third letter, fourth letter, where each attribute has the same set of values, the consonants. Table 3.1 sets forth a possible sample of positive and negative instances. How would CLS-1 develop a rule to classify them?

TABLE 3.1
EXAMPLE PROBLEM TO ILLUSTRATE CLS-1

Positive instances	Negative instances
JRTK	JVBK
QPQZ	QPWY
BRYL	NTYD
XVQM	MRQM
PTQW	JCTK
FRKV	BRQV
NSQK	LRQW

At the start of step (1), JRTK, the first positive instance, is compared with QPQZ, the second positive instance. The two have no position which contains the same letter, so step (1) fails. In step (2) the first negative instance, JVBK, is compared with the second, QPWY. Again the two have no position with a common letter, so step (2) also fails.

By counting [step (3)], it is found that in the first position no letter occurs more than once over the set of positive instances, that R occurs three times in the second position, that Q occurs four times in the third, and that no letter occurs more than once in the fourth position. Therefore Q is selected as the test characteristic for the first node.

The problem can now be split up into subproblems. Figure 3.1 illustrates the split [step (4)]. Notice that in the first subproblem the third position has been eliminated. This is because, by definition, all objects in the first subproblem have the same value for the third position, so this position need no longer be considered.

Step (5) is now executed; the entire procedure is reapplied to the first subproblem. Mathematically, the execution of the process within itself makes the CLS-1 learning computation, and all other learning computations we shall discuss, a *recursive function*. As illustrated in the Algol program (Appendix C), it can be defined in a nonrecursive fashion if this simplifies the programming.

Following step (5), attention is turned to subproblem 1. Application of

Is Q in the third position?

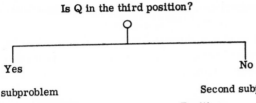

	First subproblem		Second subproblem	
Yes			No	
Positive instances	Negative instances		Positive instances	Negative instances
QP-Z	MR-M		JRTK	JVBK
XV-M	BR-V		BRYL	QPWY
PT-W	LR -Q		FRKV	NTYD
NS -K				JCTK

FIG. 3.1. Developing tree form of concept using CLS-1. Partial solution after selecting first test characteristic.

(1) again fails, since QP - Z and XV - M contain no common character-istics (except for the -, which does not count). However, at step (2) we find that MR - M, BR - V, and LR - Q all contain R in the second posi-tion, and no positive instances contain R in the second position. There-fore the first subproblem is solved. The partially developed tree representing the concept is as shown in Fig. 3.2.

Is Q in the third position?

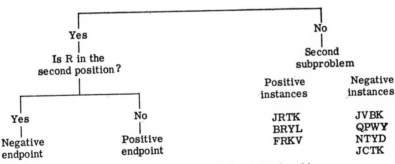

FIG. 3.2. Partial concept after solving first subproblem.

Control is now returned to step (5) at the original level, and the second subproblem attacked. Here step (1) succeeds, since all positive instances contain R in the second position and no negative instances do. No more subproblems remain, so the final concept can be stated in the form shown in Fig. 3.3. This is equivalent to the logical statement, "Positive instances are defined by the presence of R in the second position or Q in the third position, but not both." It is an example of the same structure as problem I.4_(see Chapter 2, Section 4).

A moment's reflection shows that the method just described will always produce some tree. Will it produce a simple tree, in a reasonable time? The answer is that it will if a heuristic "rule of thumb" implicit in step (3) is correct. Recall that in step (3) a frequency count is made using only the descriptions of positive instances. This obviously reduces the amount of counting required over the amount that would be needed if all descriptions were involved in the count. It provides useful information only if (a) objects designated as positive instances are more similar to each other than objects designated as negative instances are to each other and (b) this similarity has something to do with the classification rule. To illustrate

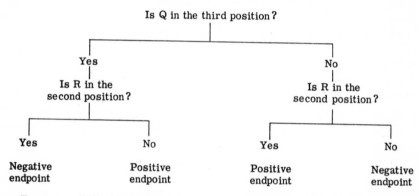

FIG. 3.3. Final form of concept developed by CLS-1 from sample of Table 3.1.

the flavor of this assumption, consider the following example: "I assume that objects called 'dogs' are, in general, more alike than are objects called 'not dogs.'" There is no logical reason that this should be so, but we offer the (undecidable) conjecture that it is true more often than not in everyday life. The assumption is neither true nor false; it can be more or less true. For instance, the superficial characteristics of dogs are generally similar, but the occasional Mexican hairless specimen gives one pause. The assumption is more nearly true for "cats" and "not cats." The power of a particular CLS will be determined in part by how sensitive it is to violations of the assumptions upon which its heuristics are based.

CLS-1 was used to solve the problems in Problem Sets I, II, and III. In addition, a variation of Problem Set I was used in which the classification rules had the same structure, but the number of irrelevant attributes and values was varied. Thus the complexity of object description was altered without changing the complexity of the correct answer. The details of these studies, all of which were conducted by appropriate programming of the IBM 7090, are presented in the following sections.

2. EXPERIMENT I

In this experiment CLS-1 solved the problems of Problem Set I. Recall that these concepts involved one, two, or three node trees representing five different concatenations of two relevant characteristics, each characteristic being the value of a different attribute. An example would be the definition, "Positive instances have value 1 of attribute 1 or value 1 of attribute 2." Complete definitions of the five problems were given in Chapter 2, Section 4.

The procedure used in Experiment I was essentially the same procedure used in all the artificial intelligence experiments, so it will be presented in some detail. A *condition* is defined as a combination of program type and problem type. In this experiment there was one program, CLS-1, and five problem types, hence five conditions. At each replication of a condition 50 objects were selected at random from the universe of 256 (4^4) possible objects. These 50 objects, in the order of their selection, define the sample. In the learning phase each member of the sequence was presented, singly and in order, to the CLS-1 program. The resulting action is diagrammed in Fig. 3.4. At the first presentation ($t = 1$) the program developed the trivial hypothesis that all objects had the same class membership as the first object presented. On subsequent trials the new object was categorized using the current concept, and its hypothetical class membership matched against its true membership. If the predicted classification was correct the object was added to memory but no further action was taken. If an error was made a new hypothesized concept was developed, based on all information in memory at that time. After the entire sequence had been presented the learning phase was terminated and the current hypothesis examined to determine how accurate it was in predicting class membership of the entire universe of 256 objects.

In Experiment I each condition was repeated 14 times. Each sample was used with each of the five problems. The data from six sequences in combination with each of the five problems were subjected to an extensive trial-by-trial examination. Only the data on number of errors and the form of the final concept were measured for the other eight sequences. Some of the individual sequences were repeated up to five times in order to measure the amount of variability due to the possibility of random choices at different points in the CLS-1 program. In no case was any variation in performance observed.

Independence of replication and independence of selection of different sequences was achieved by altering the initial value of a random number in the IPL-V translator program. The value of this number controlled pseudo-random decision operations available in IPL-V (Newell, 1964).

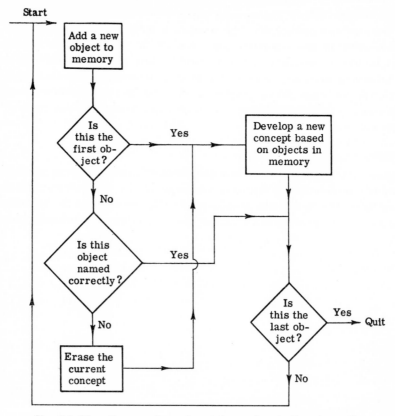

FIG. 3.4. Flow diagram of experimental procedure in Experiment I.

Three performance measures were taken: the total number of classification errors made during the learning phase, the total amount of computing effort used in developing new hypotheses, and the accuracy of the final answer when used as a rule for classifying the 256 objects of the universe. The first measure is a straightforward error count. So is the third, which is determined by calculating how many true positive instances would be classified as negatives by the final hypothesis, and vice versa. This count is then amalgamated into an error rate.

2.1 $$\text{Error rate} = \frac{\text{number of objects misclassified}}{\text{number of attempts to classify}}.$$

This can be computed for all objects in the universe, or for positive and negative instances separately.

Computing effort was measured by determining the "cycle count," the number of basic IPL-V instructions which the program executed in constructing each new hypothesis. This measure is independent of the physical characteristics of the computer used and of the characteristics of the particular IPL-V translator program used to turn the IBM 7090 into a "list processing machine." However, it is not independent of the characteristics of the particular IPL-V program used to realize CLS-1. While not an ideal measure of computing effort, the cycle count seemed the best measure readily available.

RESULTS

Figure 3.5 is a graph of the mean and standard deviation of the number of misclassifications made during the learning of the five problems. As is evident from the figure, the problems are reliably different in both the mean number of misclassifications and the variability of misclassification

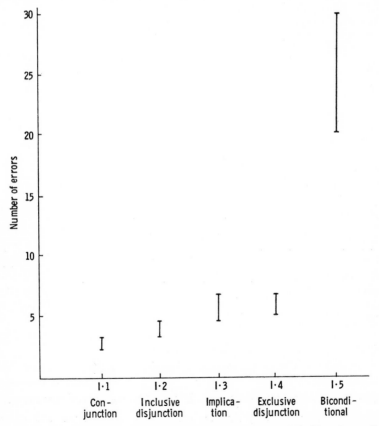

FIG. 3.5. Classification errors by problem type: mean ± 1 S.D. Experiment I.

over replication by different sequences. The overall difference between means was significant at the .01 level, using conventional analysis of variance techniques.[2]

In Chapter 2 it was pointed out that the five problems of Problem Set I fall naturally into three groups: a one-node tree, problem I.1; two two-node trees, problems I.2 and I.3; and two three-node trees, problems I.4 and I.5. Using t tests [including Snedecor's (1956) correction for unequal variance when necessary] it was shown that the problems of these three groups are reliably different between, but not within, groups. However, it is immediately clear from inspection of Fig. 3.5 that the two three-node trees are most difficult solely because problem I.5, the biconditional problem, is much more difficult than any other problem.

A somewhat different picture appears on evaluating the accuracy of the final answers. Table 3.2 presents the mean accuracy in each condition, and

TABLE 3.2

POINT OF DEVELOPMENT AND ACCURACY OF DECISION TREE DEVELOPED[a]

Problem type	Conjunction	Inclusive disjunction	Exclusive disjunction	Implication	Biconditional
Median no. of objects seen before last error	21.5	13.5	21	30	43
Mean error rate in universe	.020	.000	.000	.003	.071

[a] Average over six sequences using stimuli with four attributes and values.

the point in learning at which it was achieved. CLS-1 nearly always solved these problems by observation of a 50 object sequence. In problem I.1 (conjunction) the class of positive instances is only a small (16/256) fraction of the universe, so there is an appreciable chance that the number of positive instances in a single sequence will be so small that a very specialized answer can be developed. In a few sequences there were no positive instances at all. The resulting relatively high error rate in problem I.1 is thus an artifact of the experimental procedure, rather than due to any difficulty CLS-1 has with this problem type. Whenever there were more than three or four positive instances in the sequence, the correct tree was invariably developed.

The program tends to spend more time in computation on the more complex problems. This is hardly surprising, but the extent of the effect is. Figures 3.6–3.8 show the number of interpreter cycles required to develop

[2] Results were analyzed using Scheffe's (1959) procedure for mixed models, with sequences as a random effect.

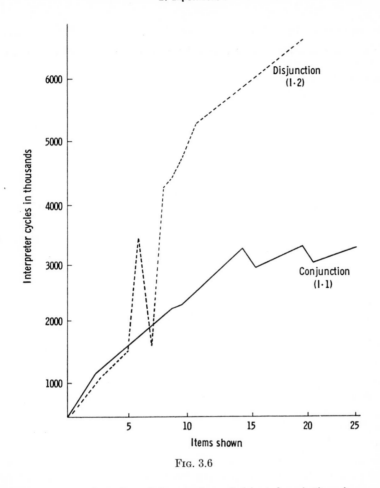

Fig. 3.6

a decision tree as a function of the number of object descriptions in memory
at the time. The relation is striking, both within and between graphs.
The data is presented in three figures since it would have been physically
impossible to present all five problems on one graph, as different scales are
needed.

Notice particularly the erratic performance on problem I.3 (implication).
Only a few errors are made on this problem, but these cause a great deal of
computation.

To get an idea of the "flavor" of concept learning by the CLS-1 system,
the successive trial concepts offered in an easy and a hard problem are
given in Figs. 3.9 and 3.10. Figure 3.9 represents the successive steps of
CLS-1 while solving one of the replications of the "easy" problem, "All
positive instances have value 1 of attribute 1 (written 1-1) and value 1

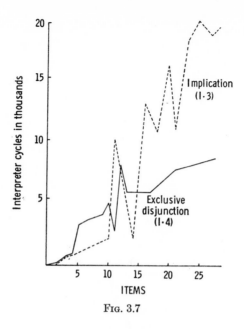

FIG. 3.7

of attribute 2 (2–1)." The first nine objects were negative instances, so the system assumed that positive instances did not exist. The tenth object was a positive instance, hence the assumption led to a misclassification. By definition, the positive instance had both characteristics 1-1 and 2-1, but it happened that the system had thus far never been shown a negative instance which had either 1-1 or 2-1 alone. Thus either of the characteristics singly, or both of them together, could be used to classify the sample. CLS-1 was programmed to "prefer" simple answers so that, by random selection, it offered the concept, "All positive instances have characteristic 1-1" (Fig. 3.9a). This worked until the twentieth object was shown. This object was a negative instance whose description contained 2-1 but not 1-1, so the first trial concept was rejected. However, both positive instances had *three* characteristics in common: 1-1, 2-1, and 4-1. This overly specific concept was offered (Fig. 3.9b). At this step CLS-1 checked and found that 1-1 and 2-1 alone did not work, but did not check to see if 1-1, 2-1, a subset of the chosen concept, would work. The twenty-first object was a positive instance *without* characteristic 4-1. Hence this was misclassified. Re-examination showed that the concept (1-1) · (2-1) could classify the sample, so it was offered as a trial hypothesis (Fig. 3.9c). This was the correct answer, so the problem was solved after three errors.

Figure 3.10 recounts the step by step progress of CLS-1 on a more difficult problem. The problem was the "biconditional classification" problem

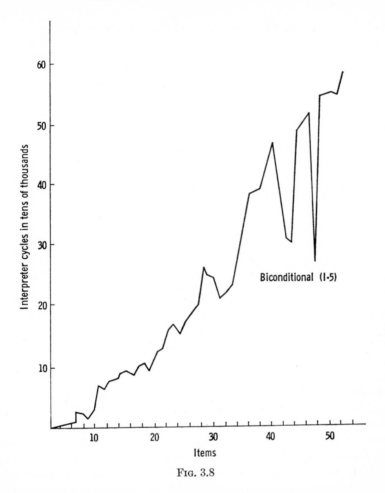

Fɪɢ. 3.8

I.5, in which all positive instances contain either *both* characteristics 1-1 and 2-1 or *neither* characteristic. CLS-1 made seven errors before offering a decision tree logically equivalent to this rule, even then it did not offer the tree of "simplest structure" (shown in Fig. 3.10h). Actually, seven errors represent rather good performance for CLS-1 on this problem, 25 errors would be more representative (see Fig. 3.5). The reason for this poor performance can be seen by examining the different trial hypotheses. Since, in this problem, positive instances did not form a homogeneous set of objects, the heuristic assumption of CLS-1 was in error. The system could not discover "good discriminators" by counting the frequency of characteristics on positive instances. Instead what it did was to build up a concatenation of simple rules for "special cases," e.g., "For objects which have

(a) CONCEPT AFTER ITEM TEN WAS PRESENTED

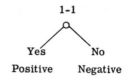

(b) CONCEPT AFTER ITEM TWENTY

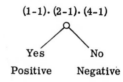

(c) CONCEPT AFTER ITEM TWENTY-ONE (CORRECT)

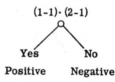

FIG. 3.9. Progressive development of concept by CLS-1. Problem I.1 (conjunction).

characteristic 1-2, check to see if they have characteristic 2-1"; "For objects with characteristic 1-3, see if they have characteristic 2-1." Note that the system has no way of checking to see that it is building up the same simple rule for each special case, since characteristic 2-1 is not, in itself, more frequently associated with positive instances than any other characteristic. As the steps shown in Fig. 3.10 illustrate, getting the correct answer depends upon obtaining within the sample at least one example of a positive and a negative instance within each of the four possible "special cases" defined by values of attributes 1 and 2. As a result, a relatively large sample was required to define the correct concept. That this is due to the operation of the system, and not to an inherent limitation on information in the sample, will be shown in subsequent chapters, when a CLS will be presented which can solve this problem more rapidly than CLS-1 although the samples presented to the two systems are the same.

3. EXPERIMENT II

The objects used in Experiment I can be completely described by stating the value of four attributes. Although these objects are rather more complex than the objects used as stimuli in many psychological studies of human

(a) TRIAL CONCEPT AFTER ITEM 3

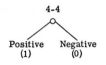

(f) TRIAL CONCEPT AFTER ITEM 25

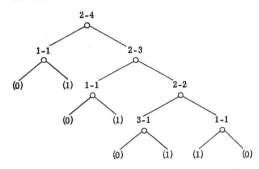

(b) TRIAL CONCEPT AFTER ITEM 6

(c) TRIAL CONCEPT AFTER ITEM 12

(d) TRIAL CONCEPT AFTER ITEM 16

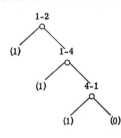

(g) TRIAL CONCEPT AFTER ITEM 31 (Final)

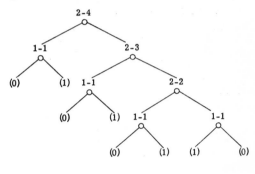

(e) TRIAL CONCEPT AFTER ITEM 18

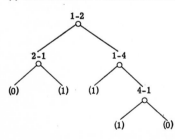

(h) SIMPLER FORM OF (g)

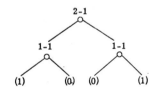

Fig. 3.10. Successive stages in development of concept by CLS-1 on Problem I.5 (biconditional). Positive instances are denoted by (1), negative instances by (0).

concept learning, they are not nearly as complex as the objects which must be categorized in everyday behavior. Consider how many ways there are in which faces can vary.

One can envisage situations in which a fairly simple underlying concept is hidden by either the presence of a large number of attributes which are irrelevant to it, or by the learner's making unnecessarily fine distinctions between the values of given attributes. The first situation is analogous to the presence of noise generators in signal detection situations, the second to the use of a nonoptimal coding scheme. To make an explicit connection between these situations and concept learning would carry us too far afield (but see Hunt (1962) and Garner (1962) for discussion of this from two different viewpoints). Within the framework of Chapter 1, the question asked concerns the effect of the complexity of the description space on the performance of CLS-1. Experiment I was repeated, with the difference that the objects, instead of being defined by four attributes with four values each, were defined by four, five, or six attributes with four, five, or six values. Thus there were nine separate conditions. Within each condition Experiment I was repeated with five replications using independent sequences. Different sequences were used in each condition.

RESULTS

Tables 3.3 and 3.4 present the results for errors during learning. Increases in description complexity generally resulted in more errors of classification.

TABLE 3.3

MEAN CLASSIFICATION ERRORS AS A FUNCTION OF PROBLEM TYPE
AND STIMULUS COMPLEXITY CONDITION: EXPERIMENT II

Problem condition	Conjunction	Inclusive disjunction	Exclusive disjunction	Implication	Biconditional
Four Dimensions					
4 values	2.25	4.75	4.25	4.25	9.50
5 values	2.00	3.25	6.00	4.00	12.00
6 values	1.25	3.50	3.75	3.75	12.25
Five Dimensions					
4 values	4.25	4.50	7.00	7.00	15.25
5 values	2.50	4.25	5.75	2.75	14.75
6 values	1.00	4.25	5.50	4.50	13.50
Six Dimensions					
4 values	1.25	4.00	7.00	6.00	18.25
5 values	2.75	3.75	6.00	4.25	12.50
6 values	0.25	4.00	5.50	4.25	15.25

However, this effect was small compared to the differences in error frequency between problems. Although further investigation would be necessary over a wider range of complexity, these results suggest that the behavior of CLS-1 in the learning phase is not greatly affected by irrelevant object complexity.

Table 3.5 presents the mean error rate for final answers. Only the results for the five and six attribute conditions are shown, the results for the four attribute condition were substantially those obtained in Experiment I. The most important effect is clearly problem type. In virtually all conditions and series the program developed the correct answers for problems I.2 and I.4. If two or more positive instances were included in the sequence, a correct answer was also developed for the conjunctive problem, I.1. As noted in discussing Experiment I, the procedure for creating sequences

TABLE 3.4
ANALYSIS OF VARIANCE OF ERROR SCORES: EXPERIMENT II

Source	D.f.	Sum of squares	ms	F
Problem type (1)	4	2945.390	736.348	121.309[a]
No. of attributes (2)	2	66.645	33.322	5.490[b]
No. of values (3)	2	42.079	21.040	3.466[c]
(1) × (2)	8	78.410	9.801	1.615
(1) × (3)	8	31.143	3.893	0.641
(2) × (3)	4	28.488	7.122	1.173
(1) × (2) × (3)	16	153.207	9.575	1.577[d]
Residual	135	819.500	6.070	—

[a] $p < .005$.
[b] $p < .01$.
[c] $p < .05$.
[d] $p < .100$.

could result in a sequence which did not contain a single positive instance, especially in the more complex stimulus conditions. The resulting high error rates for problem I.1, positive instances, are thus in a sense an artifact of the random selection procedure.

On the implication and biconditional problems (I.3 and I.5) the program's final answer was often adequate to categorize the sequence, but not the universe as a whole. On the other hand, the answer was considerably better than one obtained by chance classification. This can be seen by comparing the data of column 5 of Table 3.5 with that in column 6. Column 5 shows the mean error rate over all instances. Column 6 shows the error rate which would be obtained if a learner observed a sequence of 50 objects, then categorized all objects in the universe as members of that class most frequently observed in the sequence. This simple rule, "Regard all objects as members of the largest class, and accept the resulting errors," will be referred to as a "no computing" rule, since it provides a classification pro-

TABLE 3.5

Mean Accuracy of Final Concept: Experiment II

1. Condition	2. Problem	3. Positive instance error rate	4. Negative instance error rate	5. Mean error rate	6. Non-computing error rate
5 attrib.,	I.1 conjunction	0	0	0	.062
4 values	I.2 inclusive disj.	0	0	0	.484
.04 of	I.3 implication	0	0	0	.192
universe	I.4 exclusive disj.	0	.027	.016	.422
in sample	I.5 biconditional	.074	.083	.078	.422
5 attrib.,	I.1 conjunction	.744	0	.029	.040
5 values	I.2 inclusive disj.	0	0	0	.360
.016 of	I.3 implication	.036	.050	.038	.160
universe	I.4 exclusive disj.	0	0	0	.320
in sample	I.5 biconditional	.187	.167	.180	.320
5 attrib.,	I.1 conjunction	.957	0	.027	.027
6 values	I.2 inclusive disj.	0	0	0	.306
.006 of	I.3 implication	.074	.284	.103	.139
universe	I.4 exclusive disj.	0	.010	.007	.278
in sample	I.5 biconditional	.200	.366	.246	.278
6 attrib.,	I.1 conjunction	.498	0	.031	.062
4 values	I.2 inclusive disj.	0	0	0	.438
.012 of	I.3 implication	.014	.042	.020	.188
universe	I.4 exclusive disj.	0	0	0	.351
in sample	I.5 biconditional	.209	.362	.309	.351
6 attrib.,	I.1 conjunction	.398	0	.016	.040
5 values	I.2 inclusive disj.	0	0	0	.360
.003 of	I.3 implication	.005	.050	.020	.160
universe	I.4 exclusive disj.	0	.014	.010	.320
in sample	I.5 biconditional	.192	.290	.223	.320
6 attrib.,	I.1 conjunction	1.000	0	.028	.028
6 values	I.2 inclusive disj.	0	0	0	.311
.001 of	I.3 implication	.012	.136	.030	.139
universe	I.4 exclusive disj.	0	0	0	.283
in sample	I.5 biconditional	.254	.349	.282	.283

cedure from only the simplest possible examination of the information made available during the learning phase.

Problems I.3 and I.5 are the only problems in which the set of objects containing neither relevant characteristic is a subset of the set of positive instances. Examination of the trees developed as final answers to these problems indicated that the majority of classification errors involved erroneous designation of some members of this set as negative instances. An example is shown in Fig. 3.11.

Complexity exerted its effect in two ways. As additional attributes and values were added, the size of the sample relative to the size of the universe of objects decreased, since the sample size was held constant. The program was forced to extrapolate to a larger and larger universe without being

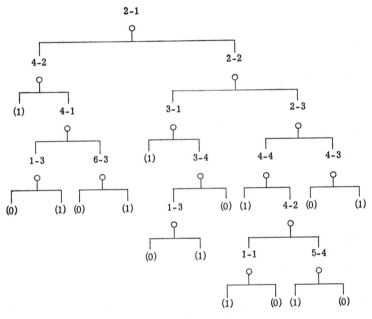

TREE PRODUCED BY CLS-1

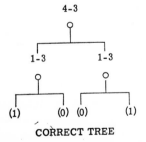

CORRECT TREE

Code; 2-1
Attribute 2, Value 1.

Left-hand branches indicate "Yes" answers to the test above them.

(1) = Positive endpoint

(0) = Negative endpoint

FIG. 3.11. Tree developed by CLS-1 when six irrelevant attributes are present. Note that the tree is overly complex because on the left-hand branch it has introduced discriminations based on the irrelevant attribute 2. Experiment II.

given a corresponding increase in the amount of information upon which the extrapolation was to be based. One would expect such a requirement to result in an increased error rate. However, the average error rate did not increase nearly as rapidly as the sample/universe ratio decreased. Consider the two extreme cases. In the six attribute five value condition the error rate for extrapolating of the decision tree to the universe, averaged over problems, was approximately three and one-half times the comparable error rate of the five attribute four value condition. The ratio of the sample/universe fraction for these two conditions is 49/1.

The effect of increased object complexity depended upon how complexity was increased. If the number of values per attribute was increased, the size of the set of objects containing neither relevant characteristic increased relative to the rest of the universe, while the relative size of the set of objects containing both characteristics decreased. Problems which include the first subset as positive instances became difficult, and problem I.1 became more difficult simply because positive instances become rare. It should be noted that this might not be true if it were not for the arbitrary restriction that every possible description be represented exactly once in the universe.

4. EXPERIMENT III

Problem Sets II and III (see Chapter 2, Section 4) represent increases in relevant complexity over the problems used in Experiments I and II. Reviewing briefly, Problem Set II contains four problem types in which positive instances are defined by a concatenation of the presence of three relevant characteristics, the values of three different relevant attributes. Problem Set III contains four problem types in which there are four relevant characteristics and four relevant attributes. Only the binary connectives *conjunction* and *inclusive disjunction* were used to define the particular combination of characteristics which served as the correct classification rule.

In addition to the relevant attributes, the objects used with Problem Sets II and III were also described by four irrelevant attributes. Both relevant and irrelevant attributes had four values each, creating universes of 4^7 objects (in Problem Set II) and 4^8 objects (in Problem Set III).

The experimental procedure and measurements were the same as in Experiment II.

RESULTS

Results are summarized in Table 3.6. The number of errors during the learning phase did not increase markedly over the number of errors made in Experiment I. The amount of computation did increase sharply, since

CLS-1 had to produce an hypothesis with more nodes, and hence make more recursions, than in the previous experiments. Also, the mere fact of there being more characteristics whose frequency must be determined will increase the number of computations involved in defining subproblems.

TABLE 3.6

MEAN ERRORS AND INTERPRETER CYCLES USED DURING LEARNING
AND ERROR RATE IN CATEGORIZATION[a]

Problem		Average number of errors while developing tree	Average computation cycles	Accuracy of tree			Error rate of no computation rule[b]
No.	Logical form			Fraction of positive instances called negative	Fraction of negative instances misclassified	Average error rate	
				Problem set II			
II.1	A · B · C	.60	2166	.996	0	.016	.016
II.2	A · (B ∨ C)	4.20	21180	.189	.006	.025	.104
II.3	(A · B) ∨ C	3.00	19529	.060	0	.017	.297
II.4	(A ∨ B) ∨ C	3.80	12604	.243	0	.140	.432
				Problem set III			
III.1	(A ∨ B) · (C · D)	2.20	15211	.534	.008	.022	.027
III.2	(A ∨ B) · (C ∨ D)	10.40	103369	.328	.021	.076	.180
III.3	(A · B) ∨ (C · D)	7.00	52864	.425	.008	.058	.121
III.4	(A ∨ B) ∨ (C ∨ D)	5.40	40210	.350	0	.239	.316

[a] Fraction of universe in sample: Problem Set I, .004; Problem Set II, .001.
Final rule: Problem Sets II and III.

[b] Assuming the larger set in the universe is also the larger set in the sample. On problems II.4 and III.4 the "no computation" rule is to call all objects positive instances. On all other problems the rule is to call all objects negative instances.

Within problem sets (thus holding the number of relevant dimensions constant) the number of classification errors and the amount of computation varied a good deal with the particular logical structure of the concept being learned. This variation, however, is smaller than the extreme "between problems" variation found in Experiments I and II. In Problem Sets II and III positive instances are always defined by different combinations of the presence of relevant characteristics, i.e., certain combinations are sufficient, although perhaps not necessary, for the identification of positive instances. In Problem Set I two problems, I.3 and I.5, include some positive instances which are defined by the absence of relevant characteristics. These problems produced either poor or highly variable performance, a factor that was not present in Problem Sets II and III.

The right hand side of Table 3.6 summarizes the accuracy of the concepts developed. In all problems except II.1 the concept developed by CLS-1 was more accurate than that offered by the "no computation" rule. The results for problem II.1 and, to a lesser extent, problem III.1, are due to the same artifact in the selection procedure which handicapped CLS-1 in learning a conjunctive concept from observation of complex objects. The set of positive instances is so small, relative to the universe, that a sample of only 50 objects (less than 1% of the universe) may not contain any positive instances. If this happens, or if only one or two positive instances are included, there simply is not enough information for any

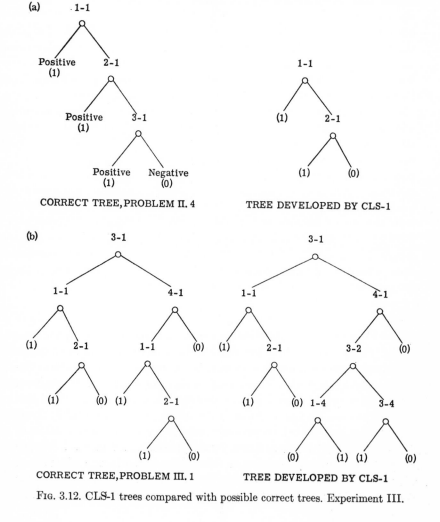

FIG. 3.12. CLS-1 trees compared with possible correct trees. Experiment III.

inductive reasoning system to do very well. The "troubles" of CLS-1 illustrated in Figures 3.9 and 3.10 are thus compounded in this experiment.

Apart from these two problems, CLS-1's answers were quite accurate considering the very small size of the sample relative to the universe. After observing less than 1% of the objects possible, CLS-1 was able to offer a decision rule adequate for categorizing correctly 75% or more of the objects in the universe.

In both Experiments II and III, CLS-1 often developed overly complex classification rules. At some stage, subproblems would be defined by variation along an irrelevant attribute. An example is shown in Fig. 3.11. The reason that this happens is that, at each subproblem, CLS-1 searches for the attribute which, loosely, exhibits the least variation over positive instances. As the number of irrelevant attributes is increased, the probability that one of these irrelevant attributes will, on a randomly chosen subproblem, exhibit a spuriously low variation is increased. It is not clear how CLS-1, or any other system which does not have some independent check on chance factors in the data given it, can avoid this.

Another aspect of CLS-1's performance which is worth commenting upon is its tendency to "undergeneralize." Table 3.6 shows that the typical error was to call a positive instance a negative one, i.e., to fail to assign a name when it should be assigned. If the correct concept involves several, possibly overlapping, rules for defining positive instances by sufficient conditions, and if only a subset of these rules is needed to categorize correctly all objects in the sample, then CLS-1 will offer as its hypothesis only the subset of sufficient rules. All items not covered explicitly are routed to a "junk" endpoint at the lower right hand leaf. In other words, the program does not consider alternate possible ways of classifying the sample once it discovers a satisfactory way. In Fig. 3.12 some typical final answers are contrasted to the correct answer, to illustrate this tendency.

5. DISCUSSION

The CLS-1 technique has been shown to be capable of developing reasonably accurate classifying rules in a complex environment. Of course, one can object that the rules are not accurate enough or that the environment is not complex enough. This is a subjective judgement. One defense to it is to point out that CLS-1 does far better than human beings do in similar environments. This will be shown in detail later. One particularly encouraging result is that CLS-1 is relatively insensitive to increases in complexity of description per se, since its major response is to complexity of structure of the correct answer. In a sense this illustrates, with an artificial intelligence, a point made quite strongly by Garner (1962) in discussing human intellectual performance—in intelligent behavior the crucial variable is not variety itself, but how the variety is related to the responses required. This point should be valid for a useful artificial intelligence device; the device should immediately grapple with the structure of relevant attributes. Insofar as possible, it should not be sidetracked into an analysis of irrelevant object variation.

How the structure of a problem affects CLS-1's performance is also clear. Every node represents, in effect, a subsidiary concept learning problem. Thus each node in the correct answer represents another opportunity for the program to designate an irrelevant characteristic for testing, and this would be true for any program operating within the CLS paradigm.

A second effect of structure, however, is due to the particular assumptions made in the CLS program. When positive instances are relatively homogeneous the heuristic assumption that positive instances have a great many common features is, by definition, correct. If it is not correct, CLS-1 will find the problem more difficult, although it still may solve it. This effect is pronounced in the more complex problems. The most striking illustration of it is the large difference in difficulty of problems I.4 and I.5, even though one is simply the negation of the other. Obviously, it would be easier to solve problem I.5, using CLS-1, if the definitions of positive and negative instances were switched. Since the relative homogeneity of positive and negative instances could be detected by direct observation, without first solving the concept learning problem, this observation could be used as a clue in deciding how the problem could be presented to a CLS-1 program.

Several changes from the CLS-1 system might provide a more efficient concept learner. One possibility is to alter the subproblem selection step of the concept learning computation to make use of the information in the set of negative instances. Another variation is to let the system itself decide, by using some criterion for finding good subproblems, which items should be regarded as "positive" and "negative" instances at any stage in problem solving. A third variation is to provide some means for constructing close to optimally information loaded sequences of objects, instead of basing hypotheses on object descriptions observed at random.

Another modification, which involves a departure from the basic CLS paradigm, is to construct a device that would construct several alternate trees, based on the first n objects presented, and then select as a test case, the $(n + 1)$st object, an object whose class membership, no matter what it is, would clearly disconfirm approximately half the hypotheses under consideration. Bayesian induction procedures could be used to specify the optimal test case (Watanabe, 1960). Such a device would be efficient in terms of the rapid development of an answer, but the cost of computing alternate hypotheses and tests for them would also have to be considered.

The cost of computing a hypothesis increases rapidly as the number of object descriptions on which it is to be based increases. This is particularly true in problems in which object descriptions are complex. The added information in large records may not be worth this added cost. Some CLS's with limited memory capacities will be investigated in Chapter 4.

All these proposals are reasonable. Most of them have the characteristic that increased accuracy is to be purchased at the cost of added complexity of computation. Gains in speed or accuracy of learning in an artificial intelligence device must be considered relative to their cost.

The Effect of Restricted Memory

1. LIMITED MEMORY SYSTEMS

The perfect, infinitely expandable memory procedures used in CLS-1 are obviously impractical, since the system could be swamped by increasing the amount of data available to it. Suppose CLS-1 were to be used as part of an automatic data processing procedure for discovering diagnostic rules based on the records of patients admitted to New York City hospitals in the past 15 years. It would take an unacceptably long time to get past the first subproblem. Similarly, human beings certainly do not consider explicitly every single case of which they have knowledge when they form their concepts. Good learners are able to operate effectively on a fairly small body of stored information.

In this chapter we report experiments with two further concept learning systems, CLS-2 and CLS-3, which differ from CLS-1 only in their memory systems. Both use the fixed size, random selection systems which were defined in Chapter 2, Section 2. Programs for both systems are presented in Appendix A, Section 3, so that it is sufficient here to review briefly the ideas behind fixed size systems.

The perfect memory system of CLS-1 assumed that there was always available room to store a record of the object presented at time t. In the first fixed size system, used in CLS-2, it is assumed instead that there are only a limited number of storage files available. Every time a new record is presented (i.e., at each trial) a file is chosen, at random, and the new record stored in it. If the chosen file contains a previously stored record, this record will be lost.

Assume that there are a total of $2k$ files available to the concept learner for such storage. In CLS-2 there is no internal organization, any record may be stored in any file. The memory used in CLS-3 provides a minimal amount of internal file structure. In it k of the files are reserved for storage of positive instances, and k separate files for storage of negative instances. Within these sets of files, however, the choice of a location in which to store a particular record is made randomly. This is a very small bit of organization, but it does introduce an important restriction. In CLS-2 the expected ratio of positive to negative instances recorded in memory is the same as the ratio of positive to negative instances in the universe. In CLS-3 this is not true, once a large sample has been observed. Eventually CLS-3 will fill up its two independent sets of files. Henceforth the same number of records of positive and negative instances will be available, since there will always be k records of each type. Within each set of files, however, the turnover of records will be more or less rapid depending on whether positive or negative instances are more often encountered in the universe. (Obviously, this is a special case of the more general situation in which k_1 files are reserved for records of positive instances and k_2 files for records of negative instances.) Before the two sets of files are full, however, the ratio of positive to negative instances in memory may vary considerably. The files reserved for the more frequent type of record will normally fill up first, and in small samples (particularly when sample size is small relative to the total number of files available) the difference between the information stored by CLS-2 and CLS-3 may not be significant. Eventually, however, CLS-3 will magnify the effects of information contained in records of objects of an infrequently encountered class, relative to the weight given such information by CLS-1 or CLS-2.

Both CLS-2 and CLS-3 stabilize concept learning in the sense that they impose a limit on the total amount of information that will be considered in evaluating an hypothesis. This limits the amount of computation that must be done following any one error. On the other hand, since it also limits the amount of information available on which an hypothesis is to be based, they may produce more faulty hypotheses than will CLS-1, given the same information. Thus it is possible that the total amount of computation could be even greater, for some problems, when fixed memory systems are used.

On logical grounds alone, one would expect that all these factors might operate, but that their relative importance would depend on the structure of the problem and the particular memory size. To get a clearer idea of the interaction between the different variables, experiments similar to Experiments I, II, and III were repeated with CLS-2 and CLS-3, using three different sizes of memory.

2. EXPERIMENT IV

CLS-2 and CLS-3 attempted the problems of Problem Set I. The design and procedure were similar to those of Experiment I. Five independent samples of 50 objects were selected. By using the concepts of Problem Set I to divide the sample into positive and negative instances, five problems were created from each sample. A problem, then, consisted of a combination of problem type and sample. As in Experiment I, objects were presented to the appropriate system one at a time. At each presentation the object's description was stored in memory, according to the rules of the CLS being used, and classified. If the classification was incorrect a new trial concept was developed, using the information in memory at that time. Three different sizes of memory, 10, 20, and 30 records, were used with each CLS. A condition thus became a combination of problem, program, and memory size. Each condition was repeated five times. This was necessary because the introduction of memory systems containing random storage rules produced variation in the performance of a given program on the same problem from repetition to repetition.

The design of the experiment can be described as a four-variable, complete factorial layout, combining sequences (five), problem types (five), CLS programs (two), and memory sizes (three), with five replications in each cell. Three of the variables—problem type, program, and memory size—are arbitrarily established, "fixed," variables. The fourth variable, sample, represents a true random variable, since the five samples used were randomly chosen from all possible orders of selection of 50 objects from the universe of 256 objects (Scheffe, 1959).

Three performance measures were taken: the number of misclassifications during the learning phase, the number of IPL-V interpreter cycles used during the development of trial concepts, and a measure of the accuracy of the final concept relative to a "no computation" classification rule. The first two measures and their rationale were described in Chapter 3. The third measure, computation gain (CG) is defined as

2.1 $$\text{CG} = 1 - \frac{\text{number of items misclassified by final concept}}{\text{minimum (positive instances, negative instances)}}$$

Recall that the simplest possible classification rule is to observe whether positive or negative instances are in the majority in the sample, and then name all 256 objects as members of this class. The number of errors which result will, obviously, be the number of errors in the smaller of the two classes. The CG score reflects the relative improvement which will be obtained if the final concept developed by a particular CLS program is used instead of the simple rule. The CG measure varies between 1 (when the final concept is the correct concept) and $-n_1/n_2$, where n_1 is the number of objects in the larger of the two classes, and n_2 the number of objects in the smaller. This is the theoretically lowest value of a CG score, and could only be reached if the final concept misclassified every object. In fact, this could never happen, since the concept would always be an accurate categorizer of those objects whose descriptions were in the system's memory at the time the concept was developed.

Results

Since there was marked heterogeneity of variance between conditions, the variance for each condition being correlated with the mean for the condition, all scores were converted by the log transformation.

2.2 $$y = \log(x + b)$$

where y is the transformed score, x the original score, and b a constant. The actual value of b was different for each measure. It was chosen so that the sum $(x + b)$ would be positive for all scores. In reporting the results, tables will be given of the mean raw scores, but all statistical analyses will be based on the transformed scores. The analyses performed are similar to those of Experiment III. Summaries are given in Appendix B, rather than in the text. All effects referred to in the text were significant at the .05 level or better.

Table 4.1 presents the average number of classification errors during learning for each combination of CLS, memory size, and concept to be

TABLE 4.1

Misclassification Errors during Learning Phase as a Function of Problem, CLS Type, and Memory Size: Experiment IV

Memory size	Program	Problem type				
		I.1	I.2	I.3	I.4	I.5
10	CLS-2	4.48	6.68	7.56	13.12	21.16
10	CLS-3	5.08	6.52	6.72	11.76	22.28
20	CLS-2	3.92	5.32	5.16	8.72	19.64
20	CLS-3	3.68	5.04	5.60	8.76	18.60
30	CLS-2	3.68	5.20	5.92	7.40	18.08
30	CLS-3	3.44	4.68	5.20	6.72	19.32

learned. (Samples, although statistically a separate variable, are logically a form of replication and need not be considered separately.)

As in previous experiments, the structure of the problem is by far the most important single factor in determining errors. The order of difficulty of problem types is the same as in Experiments I and II.

In both systems the number of misclassifications decreases as memory size increases, in a fairly uniform manner. There is little evidence to indicate that either CLS-2 or CLS-3 is a more efficient concept learner. Although CLS-3 does make fewer misclassifications than CLS-2 on 10 of the 15 combinations of memory size and problem type, the differences are small and not statistically reliable.

There appear to be no interactions between the main effects.

Next, look at the cost of computing an hypothesis. Table 4.2 summarizes the total number of cycles required during the experiment. In CLS-2 and CLS-3 the memory will fill in the later stages of the learning period, so the amount of computation required following each error will stabilize. How-

TABLE 4.2
COMPUTING EFFORT IN TERMS OF HUNDREDS OF IPL-V
INTERPRETER CYCLES: EXPERIMENT IV

Problem	Memory size (cells)		
	10	20	30
I.1			
CLS-2	51.55	56.93	55.63
CLS-3	50.32	53.60	60.22
I.2			
CLS-2	172.45	158.60	168.06
CLS-3	174.96	201.53	109.56
I.3			
CLS-2	209.34	212.30	289.86
CLS-3	221.34	284.84	136.64
I.4			
CLS-2	532.83	318.28	289.85
CLS-3	311.17	340.67	480.59
I.5			
CLS-2	1345.04	1667.79	2278.27
CLS-3	1621.42	1730.58	1954.28

ever, the content of the information in memory will be continually changing. In fact, since new computations of hypotheses only occur following an error in classification, the introduction of new information into the memory system is a necessary, although not sufficient, condition to cause CLS-2 and CLS-3 to re-examine their memories.

The results of an analysis of Table 4.2 are that (a) the amount of computation per problem increases with the complexity of structure of the problem, the most striking increase occurring between problems I.4 and I.5, and (b) the amount of computation increases with increased memory. The two different types of memory structure do not appear to differ in their effects on cost of computation. Evidently the decrease in total number of errors which accompanies an increase in memory size (Table 4.1) does not offset the increased amount of computation per error required by systems with larger memory. This indicates that there is no way of jointly minimizing errors and computations; hence, the least expensive system can only be determined if the relative costs of errors and computation are known.

Turning to an analysis of the accuracy of the final hypothesis developed under the various conditions, we find similar effects to those found for misclassification errors during learning. Table 4.3 presents the mean number of errors which would have resulted if the final hypotheses devel-

TABLE 4.3

ACCURACY OF FINAL HYPOTHESIS IN TERMS OF NUMBER OF CLASSIFICATION ERRORS AND CG SCORE[a]: EXPERIMENT IV

Problem	Memory size		
	10	20	30
I.1			
CLS-2	13.69(.14)	4.08(.74)	4.68(.81)
CLS-3	11.28(.30)	6.56(.59)	6.56(.59)
I.2			
CLS-2	0 (1.0)	0 (1.0)	0 (1.0)
CLS-3	0 (1.0)	0 (1.0)	0 (1.0)
I.3			
CLS-2	9.68(.80)	8.48(.83)	10.12(.77)
CLS-3	13.36(.72)	5.68(.88)	3.32(.93)
I.4			
CLS-2	38.80(.60)	8.56(.91)	4.80(.95)
CLS-3	15.04(.84)	1.52(.98)	.64(.99)
I.5			
CLS-2	95.56(.00)	71.96(.25)	53.04(.44)
CLS-3	101.88(−.06)	80.80(.16)	67.04(.31)

[a] CG scores given in parentheses.

oped by different combinations of program and memory size had been used to classify all 256 objects in the universe. The CG scores for each condition are also shown. In all but two cases the CG scores are greater than zero, indicating that the hypotheses developed by the CLS programs are considerably more accurate than those developed by the "no computation" rule.

Statistical analysis of the error scores of Table 4.3 (details of which are summarized in Appendix B) show the usual effect which problem type has on difficulty, with the exception that limited memory systems do rather poorly on problem I.1. This is because the number of positive instances in problem I.1 is rather small, and a limited memory system may never have more than one positive instance in its memory store at any one time. The same effect was noted in Experiments I and II, and should be considered an artifact of the experimental design, rather than a characteristic of CLS performance. Were any of the programs to be presented with a problem with structure of type I.1, but even a slightly greater number of positive instances than were found in the present experiment, the correct hypothesis would then be discovered quite easily.

Beside this, the results for final accuracy are quite straightforward. There is a steady increase in accuracy (both absolute and relative to the "no computation" rule) with increases in memory size. The principal rise appears to occur when memory size is changed from 10 to 20 files. Only in the case of problem type I.5 is performance well below perfect performance with a memory file of size 30 for both CLS programs. There appears to be no consistent difference between CLS-2 and CLS-3 with respect to accuracy, at any level of memory size.

Discussion

The results for all three measures indicate that over these problems CLS performance is a joint function of problem structure and memory size. Only memory size is under the learner's control. Increase in memory size decreased errors and increased final accuracy up to a memory size of 30 records, but the rate of increase of system performance per added storage unit apparently decreased with memory size. Increased memory size, although decreasing the number of errors during learning, increased the amount of computation following each error sufficiently so that the total amount of computation also increased with memory size.

There is no evidence to suggest that the use of separate memory subfiles for positive and negative instances, as in CLS-3, either improves or damages performance. This cannot be taken as evidence that a CLS with a more elaborate cross indexing scheme for selective storing of information would be a more or less efficient learner, but merely that the crude indexing system used here did not appear to help. Also, if sample size increased, an advantage for CLS-3 might have been shown.

3. EXPERIMENT V

In this experiment the performance of CLS-2 and CLS-3 was investigated using the more complex problems of Problem Set II. The design of the experiment was similar to that of Experiment IV. The only difference in design, other than those caused by changing the problem set, was that there were no repetitions within a given combination of sample, problem type, and memory size. Sample effects within each such combination were treated as within-conditions replications, thus providing the error term. The same measures were taken as in Experiment IV.

Only mean scores will be presented in the text. The details of the statistical analyses may be found in Appendix B.

RESULTS

Table 4.4 shows the number of misclassifications during the learning stage. As in Experiment IV, the performances of CLS-2 and CLS-3 are similar over problems and closely mirror that of CLS-1. There is a sharp

TABLE 4.4
AVERAGE NUMBER OF CLASSIFICATION ERRORS IN
LEARNING PHASE: EXPERIMENT V

Problem	Memory size		
	10	20	30
II.1			
CLS-2	.4	.8	1.8
CLS-3	1.6	.8	1.0
II.2			
CLS-2	8.0	5.8	4.2
CLS-3	8.6	5.8	4.0
II.3			
CLS-2	16.2	4.6	5.2
CLS-3	8.4	4.8	5.0
II.4			
CLS-2	7.4	4.8	4.4
CLS-3	5.6	4.6	3.0

drop in errors when memory size is increased from 10 to 20, but the further decrease in errors associated with the increase from 20 to 30 record spaces is negligible.

The scarcity of positive instances (less than 1% of the population) in problem II.1 accounts for the extremely low error rate shown for that problem. In some of the sequences chosen the CLS being used made one or no errors simply because there was only one or no positive instance in the sample. The resulting hypotheses are, of course, hardly better than the "hypotheses" generated by the "no computation" rule, since they classify all instances as negatives except the single "exception" contained in the sequence.

Table 4.5 gives the data for computation effort. Unlike Experiment IV, in this experiment the amount of computation required was not monotonically related to memory size. The over-all difference between memory sizes is not significant, but the interaction between memory sizes and problems is. The optimal memory size, in terms of minimizing the amount of computation required, is evidently determined by the problem structure. This, of course, is precisely what the learner does not know until the problem is solved.

Analysis of the computation effort figures indicated no consistent effects associated with type of program.

In Table 4.6 computation gain (CG) scores are presented for each condition studied. As usual, the largest effect was exerted by type of problem. CG score increased with memory size. Here, for the first time, a reliable effect due to CLS type was shown. CLS-3 programs had, on the average,

TABLE 4.5

MEAN COMPUTATION CYCLES IN LEARNING PHASE: EXPERIMENT V

Memory size	Problem			
	II.1	II.2	II.3	II.4
Data for CLS-2				
10	188	8,083	25,767	8,254
20	2,012	22,287	14,639	23,860
30	3,860	13,417	24,504	14,543
Data for CLS-3				
10	2,237	29,184	33,374	26,135
20	1,972	20,945	14,422	26,821
30	2,297	16,438	16,535	12,425

higher CG scores than CLS-2 programs regardless of memory size. A significant problem × program interaction indicated that this effect was selective, the greatest effect appearing for problem type II.2 [A and (B or C)], in which case CLS-3 is clearly superior at all sizes of memory.

Another way of looking at these results is to compare them with results obtained when the "perfect memory" scheme of CLS-1 is used to attack

TABLE 4.6

MEAN CG SCORES: EXPERIMENT V

Memory size	Problem			
	II.1	II.2	II.3	II.4
Data for CLS-2				
10	0	−.428	.281	.789
20	.002	.463	.667	.915
30	.003	.372	.667	.933
Data for CLS-3				
10	.002	.400	.667	.733
20	.201	.600	.667	.922
30	.004	.667	.667	.867

the same problems. If we compare Experiment I to Experiment IV, we find that CLS-1 is considerably more accurate in solving the less complex problems of Problem Set I than are the two limited memory systems. However, with the more complex problems there is less difference in accuracy of final answers, indicating that an increase in memory size beyond 30 would be of some, but not much, benefit in this situation.

DISCUSSION

If faced with the problems of Problem Set II, a rational choice of program would be CLS-3 with a memory file size of about 30. This program would not do worse than CLS-2, and might do considerably better in terms of accuracy of final answer. In fact, the accuracy of the final answer achieved after observing less than 1% of the possible 4^7 objects approaches that achieved using the perfect memory system of CLS-1.

If cost of computation were a significant factor, then there would be some argument for choosing a smaller memory file. The exact choice would depend on the trade off between computation, cost of errors of misclassification during learning, and cost of errors in the final answer. Decreasing costs by cutting down on memory size would lead to an increase in costs due to the other two factors. In fact, if computation cost alone is considered, the optimum memory size is not always the smallest, since in some problems the smaller number of errors made by CLS programs with large memories compensates for the increased amount of computation per error, thus actually decreasing total memory cost. The evidence from this experiment suggests that a memory size of about 30 is close to optimum for most problems and cost factors.

4. EXPERIMENT VI

The procedure for Experiment V was repeated exactly, using the problems of Problem Set III. It will be recalled that these problems involved concepts defined by concatenations of values from four relevant attributes, and that in addition there were four irrelevant attributes, making these objects the most complex ones dealt with in any of the experiments. The universe was thus defined by 4^8 possible descriptions, of which less than 1/1000 appeared in the sequence of 50 objects used to develop the concept for a given problem.

The same measurements were taken as in Experiment V. Statistical summaries appear in Appendix B.

RESULTS

The mean number of errors during learning in each condition is shown in Table 4.7. There is clearly a difference between problem types in the average number of errors, and a difference between programs, CLS-3 on the average producing more errors than CLS-2.

There is little evidence of variation in number of errors due to memory per se. (Analysis of raw scores for errors shows an insignificant F value for memory; analysis of log transform scores provides an F value of 3.18 on 2

TABLE 4.7
MEAN NUMBER OF ERRORS DURING LEARNING PHASE: EXPERIMENT VI

Memory size	Problem				
	III.1	III.2	III.3	III.4	Totals
Data for CLS-2					
10	1.4	9.2	6.0	5.2	21.8
20	2.6	9.0	6.6	5.2	23.4
30	1.2	8.6	8.0	6.6	24.4
TOTAL					69.6
Data for CLS-3					
10	2.0	10.4	9.0	7.6	29.0
20	2.6	8.6	9.2	6.6	27.0
30	1.6	9.2	8.2	4.8	23.8
TOTAL					79.8

and 96 d.f., a marginally significant figure.) The role of memory appears to vary with the problem; programs with larger memory files actually producing more errors on some problems, and fewer errors on others. This finding was not expected, and no explanation is offered for it. In any case, it is small compared to other effects.

Table 4.8 presents the mean scores for a number of computation cycles. Here all main effects are significant. The problem type effect, of course, reflects the differential difficulty of problems. The memory size effect is chiefly due to a slight increase in total computing effort when a memory of size 30 is used as opposed to one of size 10 or 20. Slightly more computing effort is used by CLS-3 than CLS-2 programs, probably due to the greater number of errors made by the former. The problem types by programs and the triple interaction (problem types × program types × memory size) variables are also significant at the .05 level. Again, these interactions were not expected and no explanation is offered for them.

Table 4.9 presents the CG scores. Owing to the added complexity of these problems, the scores were much lower than those obtained previously. The CLS systems used were evidently being strained "to the limit" in attempting to extrapolate rules based on only 50 objects.

TABLE 4.8
MEAN NUMBER OF COMPUTATION CYCLES: EXPERIMENT VI

Memory size	Problem				
	III.1	III.2	III.3	III.4	Totals
Data for CLS-2					
10	6,632	62,216	45,941	29,757	164,546
20	6,405	65,609	19,661	19,275	110,950
30	2,920	62,589	52,731	33,650	151,890
TOTAL					427,386
Data for CLS-3					
10	2,803	46,783	41,374	25,631	116,591
20	5,025	77,835	59,918	30,144	172,922
30	3,678	86,970	49,238	14,867	154,753
TOTAL					444,266

The only variables which are significant are problem types and program types, although the F value for memory size approaches significance $(.05 > p > .10)$. In practically every condition CLS-2 produces a more accurate final hypothesis than CLS-3, and in every condition CLS-2 is as

TABLE 4.9
MEAN CG SCORE: EXPERIMENT VI

Memory Size	Problem			
	III.1	III.2	III.3	III.4
Data for CLS-2				
10	.100	.590	.322	.223
20	.115	.278	.031	.223
30	.229	.620	.402	.223
Data for CLS-3				
10	−3.949	−.086	−.798	.223
20	−1.090	.067	−.408	.223
30	.029	.468	.287	.223

or more accurate than the "no computation" rule. The largest gain in memory size appears to be achieved by going from a file size of 20 to one of size 30, suggesting that still larger memory files would result in more accurate performance.

DISCUSSION

In hindsight, it probably would have been better to have performed this experiment with a larger sample. Examination of the sequences drawn and the trees developed indicates that in each sequence only a few of the possible endpoints of the correct concept had representatives (i.e., objects routed to them) in the sample. Since each endpoint represents a subclass of positive (negative) instances, a CLS must have at least one representative of each endpoint within its memory at the time it develops its final hypothesis if this subclass is to be properly differentiated by the final hypothesis. This seldom happened, and happened rather less often with CLS-3 because this system, in which half the memory was reserved for the smaller of the class of positive or negative instances, actually had less space available to record examples of different types of the larger class. How this could be remedied by proper assignment of memory space before the correct answer is known is a question to which the answer is not clear. It is obviously an important question in any inductive problem solving process. Some sort of special provision must be made for storing records which are "information rich," in the sense that they represent a particular type of object for which special classification rules are needed. But how is a concept learner to identify such a case before the "general" and "special" classification rules are known?

5. COMMENT ON LIMITED MEMORY SYSTEMS

In the problems investigated here the introduction of limited memory systems had two effects: the number of objects which had to be observed before the correct classification could be offered increased, and the amount of computation required in developing trial hypotheses decreased. In general, the latter effect more than offset the former, so that the total amount of computation needed before achieving a given level of "correctness" of hypothesis decreased with smaller memory sizes. Obviously, this could continue only up to a point.

In fact, for any given problem there is a limited memory size which a CLS must have if the problem is to be solved. To see that this is so, consider the case in which the smallest tree form of the correct concept requires n endpoints. This means that the CLS must, to develop this concept, have space for at least n records, one representing each endpoint. In general, however, n records will not uniquely define the concept. A CLS which uses a heuristic technique for "guessing" a simple structure will probably require more than n examples before it can solve the problem. The question is, "How many more?" While the details of our results are undoubtedly specific to the problems we used, the general trend of our data indicates that simple CLS's can solve relatively complex problems with rather small memory systems.

In support of this, it is interesting to note that Kochen (1961a) reports some similar results. He developed computer programs for solving conjunctive concept learning problems based on a description space with binary attributes. That is, each of the objects he dealt with could be described by the presence or absence of each of n characteristics, and hence represented by an n bit binary number. Kochen's programs were, like ours, algorithms in the sense that they were guaranteed to develop the correct answer eventually, and heuristics in the sense that they offered a solution which had a "good chance" of being correct before this solution could be proven to be the only acceptable hypothesis. Kochen found that by storing records of up to 128 previously presented objects he could achieve virtually as good performance as he achieved with a perfect memory system. Taken together with our results, this is further evidence that quite reasonable concept learning programs can be designed without introducing impossible requirements on memory.

It must be remembered that we have investigated only one type of limited storage memory system. In the CLS-2 and CLS-3 programs, and in Kochen's work, the program retains all the information about some of the items shown it. The logic is essentially that of statistical sampling. To assess the effect of advertising, give "depth" interviews to a few of the people exposed to a publicity campaign. Three other storage systems are worth mentioning, although we have not done any computations involving them.

One way to store information is to break up the record describing each instance into parts (the values of particular attributes are suitable units) and store these parts separately. If the mechanics by which information drops out of the system affect the parts independently, then at some later date the system will have available to it some information about many objects, rather than all information about a few objects. Intuitively, human memory seems to have some characteristics of such a system. Think of the times when you can recall that X is a tall, fair haired man whose name escapes you, or of the frustrating phenomenon of recalling part of a telephone number. A model of human memory which incorporates this feature has been developed (Hunt, 1963) and could perhaps be built into a CLS. To date this has not been done, and it is not clear what the effect would be on a CLS intended to perform as an artificial intelligence.

A second alternative is to ignore the co-occurrence of values of different attributes. Instead, keep track of the frequency with which particular values of attributes appear in the descriptions of positive or negative instances. The sort of classification rules which develop from such records consist essentially of weighting schemes, an object gets x "points" if it contains value one of attribute one, y points for value three of attribute two, and so on. Negative scores are allowed. If the total "point score" exceeds a certain value, the object is classified as a positive instance.

The logic of this method is the same as the logic of the statistical method of linear discriminant analysis. Many pattern recognizers operate in this manner, which Selfridge (1959) has called the "Pandemonium" procedure. Every attribute contributes something to the classification, the final classification is determined by keeping track of how accurate the contribution of each attribute has been in the past. For many purposes this is all the record that is needed, since several variations on this method can be developed. [Sebesteyen (1962) and Uhr (1963) develop the method and give examples of various programs which use it.] Thus, storage requirements are small. The method is clearly the best (it can be proven mathematically to yield the most efficient solution) if the distribution of objects into positive and negative instances is such that one can visualize a plane dividing the description space in such a way that the descriptions of all positive instances fall on one side of the plane and the descriptions of all negative instances fall on the other side. Classification reduces to the task of locating the plane. The method is weak, however, in situations in which no such plane exists. For example, in problem I.4 (the exclusive disjunction problem) it is the joint presence *or* joint absence of two characteristics which determines classification. How one should react to the value of the first attribute depends on what the value of the second attribute is. In solving such problems some record of the joint occurrence of values of different attributes is needed, not just a weighting of each attribute independently.

The final memory system which we consider represents a more radical departure from the CLS-2 and CLS-3 recording systems. No information whatsoever is stored concerning either individual items or the frequencies of occurrence of particular characteristics within different classes of items. Instead, all memory resides in the current hypothesis. Assume that this is represented as a tree. Suppose an error is made on trial t. The current tree, instead of being destroyed (as is done in CLS programs), is altered just enough so that the classification of the item at trial t is changed from incorrect to correct. This means that only those segments of the tree which lie in the path actually used in classifying the tth object are liable to change. The rest of the tree remains the same. Now the change at time t may result in a backward step, and the tree might now misclassify some items which it previously had classified correctly. If these are presented again, and the error made, the tree will be remodified. Hopefully, if efficient remodification techniques are used, the tree will become a stable, accurate representation of the correct concept.

This method has been used by Feigenbaum (1961) to simulate the processes of human verbal learning. The tasks Feigenbaum has studied are sometimes considered to be close to human concept learning, although a question can be raised as to whether the same psychological processes are involved (see, especially, Shepard *et al.*, 1961). To our knowledge, an artificial intelligence system for concept learning in which both memory for previous evidence and the current hypothesis are stored within the same classification tree has not been reported. Notice that using this sort of memory would require a reformulation of all the other processes of a CLS program, since they all assume that a record of specific instances is present. This is not to say that such a system would not work. Certainly the economy of storage which it represents seems a desirable feature, although it does raise the possibility of proliferation of an excessively complex tree. We would welcome a comparison between a concept learning system of this type and the CLS programs which we have reported.

The memory systems just described raise some other questions about possible concept learning programs which go beyond the limited problem of information storage. At the same time, it is clear that all the questions that could be raised about the role of memory in CLS programs have not been raised, let alone answered. What has been clearly shown is that the CLS programs do not require a perfect, infinite memory in order to perform well. With this in mind, we now turn to the analysis of changes in other sections of a CLS program.

CHAPTER 5

Changes within CLS Heuristics

1. SELECTIVE SAMPLING

The two preceding chapters discussed programs which varied in the amount of information retained, but used the same techniques to acquire information and to manipulate information when it was available. In this chapter the effects of changing these parts of the program are explored.

In CLS-1, CLS-2, and CLS-3 the program observes a sequence of randomly chosen objects. The program itself has no control over the order in which objects are introduced to it. The succinct phrase of Bruner *et al.* (1956), "bench bound lecture goer," defines the frequency and disadvantages of this sort of learning. In theory, a concept learner ought to be able to plan a sequence of observations which would provide more information than a sequence of random observations of the same length, but in any practical scheme two limitations must be kept in mind. The evidence we have obtained suggests that these are fatal to any scheme for developing a concept learner which provides itself with an "efficient course" in concept learning.

A scheme for selecting a sample must not presuppose knowledge of the correct answer to the problem being attacked. Columbus did not take the most efficient route to the New World because he did not know the way. Similarly, after a series of scientific studies, practically every experimenter will say, "Knowing what I know now, I would have done the fourth experiment second," or words to that effect. The same principles apply to learning by an artificial intelligence. It is obvious that, given the concept, one could construct a "course" which would lead a given CLS program to the answer after a minimum number of observations. It is not so obvious that given a sample and a (perhaps erroneous) trial concept the CLS could, itself, select the best item to try to classify next.

The second limitation is that the selection procedure must be an inexpensive one. Although we do not normally think of it this way, problem solving is an expensive affair. The results of any thought process must justify the cost which the process entails. Full consideration of the "cost of thinking" would lead us far afield, but some discussion of the problem is necessary. Consider a simple case. CLS-x and CLS-y are two unspecified computer programs. On problems of a given type CLS-x spends 20 minutes computing time determining an optimum sample, and then produces a concept of some acceptable level of accuracy. CLS-y accepts a random sample, but to produce a concept of the same level of accuracy it requires twice as large a sample as does CLS-x. Which program is better? Considering only computer time, CLS-x is better than CLS-y if and only if the total time spent determining and evaluating the optimum sample is less than the time CLS-y spends evaluating a large, suboptimal sample. If expenses other than computation time are considered the example becomes more complicated, but the basic point remains.

Two types of information are available to a CLS during concept learning: a knowledge of the description space and a knowledge of the current trial concept. Two programs were written, CLS-4 and CLS-5, which used this knowledge to construct a "cheap" criterion for selecting the next object to be added to the sample. In all other respects, the two programs were identical to CLS-1.

In CLS-4 areas of the description space were selected for examination by "exploring" points around the point at which an error was made. The distance between two objects was defined as the number of attributes on which the two objects have different values. Thus the distance between (large, brown, bear) and (large, black, bear) would be 1, the distance between (large, brown, bear) and (small, black, dog) would be 3. Objects were added to the sample according to the following rules:

(a)   The first object was selected at random.

(b)   Further objects were selected at random until an error in classification was made.

(c)   Following an error, the next object added to the sample was taken from the set of objects closest to the erroneously classified object but not yet in the sample.

Note that the trial concept used to classify the object thus selected will be the one developed *after* the erroneously classified object was added to the sample. Depending on whether or not this concept gave a correct classification, rule (b) or rule (c) (with the new object playing the role of the error) was applied.

A program for selecting a sample in this manner is shown in Appendix A, Section 3.

CLS-4 thus builds trial hypotheses which work in particular regions of the description space, then moves, randomly, to another region of the space, where it then tries out its new trial concept. When an error is encountered the new concept is tested on items similar to those which produced the error. The criterion of similarity, however, is rather loose. No particular attribute is singled out as being more "important" than others, as doing so would imply that the CLS knew something about the correct answer. (The possibility that the CLS could acquire probabilistic information about the relevance of particular attributes has not been explored.) Finally, no ordering property of the values of attributes has been assumed. CLS-4 is as likely to go from (large, brown, bear) to (small, brown, bear) as to (medium-size, brown, bear). To investigate such an environment is consistent with the general definition of CLS problems, but one can easily envisage situations in which a CLS could use to advantage some knowledge of the ordering of values of an attribute.[1]

CLS-5 uses the current trial concept as a guide to selection of the next instance. When a concept is stated in tree form, the universe is actually split into several subclasses, each subclass consisting of objects which are routed to a particular endpoint in the tree. By definition, if the trial concept is the correct answer each subclass will contain only positive or negative instances. If a classification error occurs, this is an indication that one of the subclasses contains both positive and negative instances. The program then re-orders the subclasses by creating a new tree, adequate to classify all objects seen so far, including the one on which it has just erred. The error producing object will be routed to some endpoint in the new tree. CLS-5 regards this endpoint as suspect, and tests it at the next trial. By examining the set of objects not yet seen, CLS-5 selects a new object which is routed to the suspect endpoint. This object is classified on trial $t + 1$. If the classification is correct, the "suspect" label is dropped from the endpoint and subsequent objects chosen at random until a new classification error occurs. If the classification is incorrect, a new trial concept is devel-

---

[1] The CLS-4 procedure closely resembles the technique sometimes described as "hill climbing," attempting to find the maximum value of a function of n arguments by observing the value of the function for a specific set of arguments, then altering each argument slightly in order to determine which alteration leads to the greatest positive change in the value of the function. Changes are made in the arguments until no change can be found which will increase the value of the function. If the function has only one maximum, then it will be located. However, if there are local maxima, the procedure may become stabilized at one of these instead of at the over-all maximum value. A more complete description is provided by Minsky (1961).

CLS-4 is similar in that a decision rule can be regarded as a function whose arguments are the form of the function and the values of the attributes of the object being classified. The value of the function is 1 if the classification is correct, 0 otherwise. By searching randomly through the description space, CLS-4 attempts to locate minima. When it finds one, it makes changes in the decision rule in order to eliminate this minimum and any similar minima near it.

oped (using all information now available), a new suspect endpoint indicated, and the procedure repeated.

The CLS-5 technique is illustrated in the example shown progressively in Fig. 5.1. The correct answer is, "All positive instances have either value 1 of attribute 1 (1-1) or value 1 of attribute 2 (2-1)." At the point at which

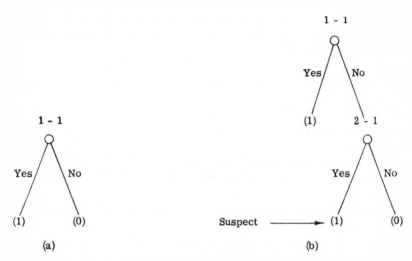

Fig. 5.1. Example of CLS-5 selection techniques. (a) Initial concept. Object (1-3, 2-1, 3-3, 4-2) is selected and misclassified. (b) New (correct) concept. The labeled endpoint is tested by classifying object (1-4, 2-1, 3-1, 4-1).

the example begins, CLS-5 has a trial concept, "Positive instances all have value 1 of attribute 1," (shown in Fig. 5.1a). The object with description (1-3, 2-1, 3-3, 4-2) is shown and classified as a negative instance. This is in error, so a new tree is grown. Suppose it is, in fact, the correct concept (shown in Fig. 5.1b). Object (1-3, 2-1, 3-3, 4-2) will be routed to the suspect endpoint on the new tree. To test this endpoint CLS-5 selects object (1-4, 2-1, 3-1, 4-1), which is also routed to this endpoint. The test object is categorized, correctly, as a positive instance, so the next object is chosen randomly.

A program for the CLS-5 selection procedure is given in Appendix A, Section 3.

2. EXPERIMENT VII

CLS-1, CLS-4, and CLS-5 were used to solve the five problems in Problem Set I. These problems were used, rather than the more complex problems of Problem Sets II and III, for two reasons. It is easier to compare CLS programs when they all reach the same (correct) answer with varying amounts of effort than to compare programs which produce different wrong answers with different amounts of effort. Also, as was illustrated in Chapter 3, the amount of computing involved in applying a CLS program to Problem Sets II and III is considerable. This would be compounded by the computations involved in applying the selection techniques of CLS-4 and CLS-5 to universes containing 4^7 and 4^8 different objects. While such an experiment might be worth the expense, one would only be justified in going on with it if positive results were first obtained in the simpler situations provided by Problem Set I.

PROCEDURE

A *condition* was defined as a combination of problem and program type. Each condition was repeated with five independent samples. At each replication the first object was chosen at random, and the trivial "concept" developed that all objects were members of the same class as the first object. From that point onward selection, classification, and the selections following errors were performed according to the rules of the CLS being used.

Two measures were taken, the number of classification errors being made and the number of objects observed before the program developed the correct answer. Sampling was continued until the problem was solved.

RESULTS

Figures 5.2 and 5.3 show the means and standard deviations for each of the 15 conditions on each of the two measures. Although the two selection-procedure programs, CLS-4 and CLS-5, make slightly fewer errors and require slightly fewer instances to define a concept than does CLS-1, this difference does not approach statistical significance. (An analysis of variance showed that the F ratios for program types and the interaction of program types and problems were both less than 1.00. Appendix B contains the relevant tables.) The statistically significant effect due to problems is clear. It is essentially the same effect obtained with CLS-1 alone (shown in Fig. 3.5 for a larger experiment); problem difficulty increases with an increase in tree complexity.

Although the size of this experiment is rather small, the results give no encouragement whatsoever to the notion that improving a CLS's selection system would improve its performance to any great extent. Note that we are not saying that larger experiments would not show statistically reliable superiority for CLS-4 or CLS-5 over CLS-1, or that such experiments would not indicate a difference between the two more sophisticated programs. Neither are we suggesting that more complex selection procedures would be fruitless. What the results do say is that the effects of changing other

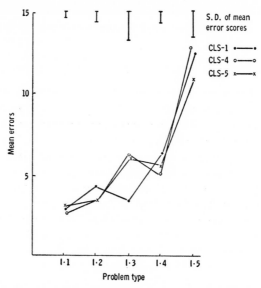

FIG. 5.2. Means and standard deviation of error scores in Experiment VII.

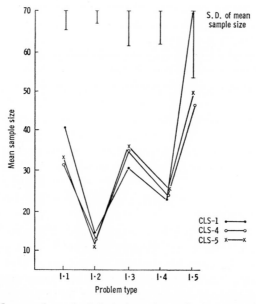

FIG. 5.3. Means and standard deviations of sample sizes. Experiment VII.

components of CLS programs should be explored first. We now turn to a change which does appear to alter system performance in an interesting way.

3. ALTERNATE SUBPROBLEM SELECTION TECHNIQUES

The subproblem selection technique of CLS-1, defining subproblems by determining that characteristic most frequently found in the description of positive instances, was chosen for its simplicity and because it seemed, intuitively, to be a reasonable way of solving "real life" concept learning problems. The method gives reasonably good results so long as its assumptions are satisfied, but leads to rather drastic deterioration of performance on problems (e.g., the biconditional problem, I.5) where they are not.

Recapitulating briefly, the CLS-1 subproblem definition technique was (a) if a conjunctive solution to the problem could be found, it was used, but (b) if no conjunctive solution could be found, a frequency count was made of the appearance of every possible value of every possible attribute in the description of positive instances, and the characteristic with the highest frequency in the set of *positive instances only* was selected as the test at the current node in the tree. Two new subproblems were then set up, the one at the lower left being to find a concept for all instances, both negative and positive, containing in their description the selected characteristic, and the one at the lower right being to find a concept with which to classify the remaining objects.

One objection to CLS-1 is that the criterion for selection of a test is a poor indicator of the test's probable utility as a class identifier, since the characteristic most frequently applicable to positive instances may often also be the characteristic most applicable to negative instances. To take a somewhat trivial example, suppose we were trying to develop a concept of the difference between dogs and cats, and we included in the description space the attribute "number of feet." CLS-1, or any of the other programs discussed to this point, might very well develop as their first question the remark, "Does the animal have four feet?" This would not get the program very far, since both dogs and cats generally have four feet. The program does not consider this.

One way to avoid such problems is not to include inane attributes in the description space. This is not entirely satisfactory as a general solution (although it may be quite practical in specific cases) because it puts the burden of defining "inane" on the program user rather than the program. An artificial intelligence system ought not to do this. Any *a priori* ruling out of an attribute implies some knowledge of the concept before the problem is solved, and this is what we are trying to do without. The problem is particularly tricky because an attribute which transmits a great deal of information about some of the objects to be classified, and thus is a useful distinction in some parts of the decision tree, may be quite useless in making other distinctions.

A better solution is to let the program select trial characteristics and subproblems on the basis of the relative frequency of occurrence of characteristics applicable to both positive and negative instances, rather than on the basis of absolute frequency. But how to define "relative frequency?" Several techniques have been suggested. We shall present three and explore one. Each of the techniques is progressively more complex, and would require additional computations. Therefore, as in the case of added memory or special selection techniques, the more complex programs must show that they can justify their costs. The class of programs which react to relative frequency are, themselves, quite expensive. Since the relative frequency of a characteristic cannot be determined without knowing its absolute frequency in both the set of positive and the set of negative instances, such programs must examine roughly twice as much data at each node as do programs CLS-1 through CLS-5.

Perhaps the simplest way to define relative frequency is to subtract the number of occurrences of a characteristic in negative instances from the number of occurrences in positive instances. This was the definition used in CLS-6, a program which was identical to CLS-1 in all other respects. At each test node at which a conjunctive solution could not be applied the program counted the number of times a characteristic appeared in the description of positive instances active at that node, then subtracted from this number the number of times the characteristic appeared in the description of negative instances. The characteristic with the maximum difference was made the test. Suppose that there are N different characteristics based on A attributes, n_1 positive instances, and n_2 negative instances being considered in the particular test node. The CLS-6 procedure requires A $(n_1 + n_2)$ observations of the value of an attribute, and N subtractions. The CLS-1 procedure, on the other hand, requires only An_1 observations.

Another definition of relative frequency compares the ratios, (frequency of occurrence on positive instances)/(frequency of occurrence on negative instances), for each object, and chooses the maximum ratio characteristic. (A trivial modification of either the subtraction or the ratio rule is to choose the absolute difference, or the maximum of the ratio just defined or its inverse, as the quantity on which to base the choice.) The problem with using a ratio rule is that ratios are statistically unstable when the smaller of the two frequencies approaches zero. For example, if characteristic a appeared on 212 of 216 positive instances and only 12 of 195 negative instances, while characteristic b appeared on five positive instances and no negative instances, the ratio rule would choose b as a trial characteristic in preference to a. Because of this possibility, no CLS program using a ratio rule for defining subproblems was completed.

An example of the effect different rules would have on subproblem definition is shown in Table 5.1.

TABLE 5.1

EXAMPLE OF CLASSIFICATION PROBLEM WITH FIRST NODE TESTS
SELECTED BY DIFFERENT SUBPROBLEM DEFINITION RULES

Object	Size	Color	Type	Class
1	Big	Red	Tomato	Edible
2	Big	Green	Cucumber	Edible
3	Big	Red	Apple	Edible
4	Small	Red	Pepper	Edible
5	Small	Yellow	Tomato	Not edible
6	Small	Green	Squash	Not edible
7	Big	Green	Tomato	Not edible
8	Big	Green	Pepper	Not edible

First node tests selected: by CLS-1, Big; by CLS-6, red; by ratio rule, red or apple.

Two other criteria, neither of which were programmed in the studies we report (but both of which are worth further investigation), should be mentioned here. These are more elegant mathematical and statistical criteria on which subproblem selection may be based. They have the advantage that they can be used in other than binary branching trees, and the disadvantage that they require more computation.

The *chi-square criterion* defines the attribute to be tested as that attribute which maximizes the value of the contingency chi-square in a two by n table in which the categories are, for the two level dimension, positive and negative instances, and for the n level dimension, the n values of the attribute. This is easily shown by example. The sample data of Table 5.1 can be used to generate Table 5.2, in which values of three attributes are cross classified with classification of object for each attribute. A contingency chi-square value can be calculated for each of these tables, using conventional statistical techniques (e.g., Snedecor, 1956). The attribute chosen for testing is that attribute which maximizes the chi-square value, and the node may have as many branches below it as the attribute has values in the population of objects being examined. An example, using the attribute "type of plant," is shown in Fig. 5.4.

The *maximum transmitted information* criterion involves almost identical computations. The same two by n tables are made up as in the chi-square method, but the two dimensions (class membership) and (attribute) are thought of as signals. Using the information theory definition of "shared information" (cf. Garner, 1962; Luce, 1960), the attribute which transmits

TABLE 5.2

Two by n Classifications of Class Membership against
Values of Attributes Using Example of Table 5.1

Attribute	Value	Edible	Not edible
Size	Big	3	2
	Small	1	2
Color	Red	3	0
	Green	1	3
	Yellow	0	1
Type of plant	Tomato	1	2
	Cucumber	1	0
	Apple	1	0
	Squash	0	1
	Pepper	1	1

the most information about an object's class membership is selected. The computations are nearly identical to those involved in the chi-square computation, and the result may be used to create a tree with nonbinary branches. We have not explored the question of whether or not the two

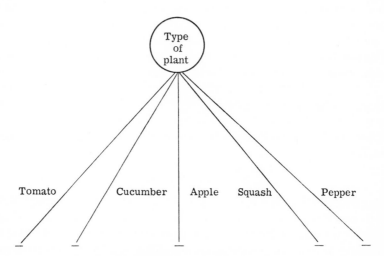

Fig. 5.4. Example of multibranching tree.

criteria will invariably lead to the same choice of a test attribute, although it is clear that they will often be equivalent. (For some related comments, see Attneave (1959, pp. 43–49 and 63–67).) The two mathematical selection techniques were not programmed because of the complexity of introducing them, with the corresponding numerical calculations and table look-up operations, into an IPL-V program.[2]

4. PROBLEM REDEFINITION

CLS-6 attempts to overcome the disadvantages inherent in CLS-1 by utilizing information about relative frequency of occurrence. It does this at the cost of added complexity. We have indicated that still more information could be utilized at still greater cost. Two further programs were written which represent an attempt to improve on CLS-1 performance with only a very small increase in program complexity. This is done by retaining the simple subproblem selection criterion of CLS-1, but by permitting the program to redefine positive and negative instances. Specifically, in CLS-7 the program is presented with two sets of objects which have (perhaps arbitrarily) been labeled "positive" and "negative." The program redefines these labels, calling the *larger* of the two sets of objects "positive instances." The CLS-1 procedure is then applied. The result is that CLS-7 is biased toward finding, first (i.e., on the left hand side of its decision tree) endpoints which can be utilized for a large number of objects in its sample. In CLS-8 exactly the opposite rule is used and the program applies the CLS-1 technique after assuming that the *smaller* of the two sets is the set of positive instances. The rationale for this is that it is more useful to look for uniformities within a small set than within a larger one.

There seems to be no *a priori* reason why either of these rules, or the CLS-6 procedure, should be better than the others. However, it turned out that they did express different degrees of sensitivity to variations in the logical structure of the problems they were required to solve. This was shown in Experiment VIII, which is reported in Section 5.

Appendix A, Section 3, gives the detailed programs for CLS-6, CLS-7, and CLS-8.

5. EXPERIMENT VIII

Experiment VIII was a replication of Experiment VII using CLS-6, CLS-7, and CLS-8. As in Experiment VII, CLS-1 was used as a control. The five problems of Problem Set I were used, with five replications of each problem-program combination. Sampling was continued randomly, one object at a time, until the correct answer was offered. Two measures

---

[2] When the research program was begun it was thought that a concept learning system would necessarily have to be defined recursively, and that realizing a CLS as a computer program would require very sophisticated memory allocation techniques. Eventually, it was found that this was not required. Section 7 describes a CLS which was constructed using conventional programming techniques.

were taken, the number of errors and the number of objects placed in the sample before the correct concept was developed.

Figures 5.5 and 5.6 present the data for mean errors and mean size of sample, respectively. Variances were of the same order as shown in Figs. 5.2 and 5.3. An analysis of variance of these measures (details in Appendix B) showed that two effects were significant, the type of problem and the

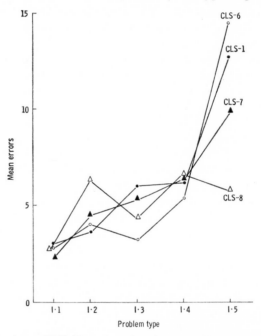

Fɪɢ. 5.5. Experiment VIII. Errors as a function of problem and program type.

interaction of problems with programs. The latter effect was significant for errors at better than the .01 level, and for size of sample at better than .025. This is the basic difference between the results of this experiment and the results of Experiment VII. In Experiment VII the effects of the different selection techniques were essentially parallel. A problem that was hard for one CLS was hard for them all. This is emphatically not the case in Experiment VIII. Although the results do not, *on the average,* demonstrate that any one CLS program is superior to any other, they do indicate that depending on the nature of the problem, a considerable advantage may be gained by using the best program for that problem. For instance, CLS-8 would be the worst choice of a program to solve a problem whose answer was a simple disjunction (problem I.2) but would be the best choice for solving a problem whose answer was a biconditional concept (problem I.5).

 This faces the potential user of a CLS program with something of a paradox. Depending upon the type of problem, he should use a particular program. He does not know what the type of problem is until he applies a program to solve the problem. What should he do? The evaluation of

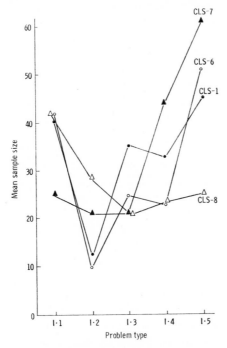

Fig. 5.6. Sample size. Experiment VIII.

experimental results in such a situation involves some as yet unsatisfactorily resolved questions in decision theory, and particularly in policies for games against Nature. In the following section we interrupt our description of experiments to discuss the decision problem in some detail. The narrative is resumed in Section 7.

6. APPLICATION OF A DECISION CRITERION TO EXPERIMENT VIII[3]

 This section is concerned with ways to evaluate the cost of problem solving. Naturally, we are concerned with a particular type of problem solving, the type required in the experiments we have just described. To

---

[3] Many of the ideas in this section were derived from suggestions by Professor Jacob Marschak of the University of California, Los Angeles, who made extensive comments on the decision problems posed by results like those of Experiment VIII. Professor Marschak has not been involved in the preparation of this book, and responsibility for any misrepresentations or errors in this section rests solely with E. B. H.

avoid confusion the level of generality at which our remarks are intended should be made explicit. We are going to describe a way of evaluating the results from a series of experiments in which the performance characteristics of two or more devices are compared under different conditions and with more than one criterion measure. The fact that we do this to evaluate computer programs should not mask the wider applicability of the method. It could equally well be defined as a rational technique for choosing cars or even (if the data were available) wives.

By using the evaluation method, we shall reach certain conclusions about CLS programs. These conclusions are forced on us by the way the method treats data obtained in specific experiments, and from CLS programs with precisely defined logical properties. The figures we obtained depended in part on certain pseudo-random events, so that the usual cautions concerning evaluation of statistical evidence are appropriate. In this we are no different from anyone else who relies on data with less than perfect reliability. We cannot use a mechanistic logic to defend any generalization of our conclusions beyond the experiments we have conducted, with programs logically identical to the ones we used. In our own defense, we think that this is always true. A generalization based on any series of experiments contains the implicit assumption that the situation to which the generalization is being applied does not differ in any important way from the situation in which the original data were obtained. This assumption is seldom right or wrong; it is more or less correct.

There are two special aspects of our experimental situations which do not affect the results and need not be considered in making generalizations. We used a particular programming language (IPL-V) and a particular computer (the IBM 7090). Our evaluation will be based on statistics concerning the number of classification errors made and the number of observations required before reaching error-free performance. These statistics are neither machine nor language dependent.

Having issued our *caveats*, let us turn to the problem at hand. Abstractly, we wish to find an optimum strategy in a game against Nature. Such games have been the topic of a good deal of extensive investigation, but no completely satisfactory way of determining the optimal policy has yet been enunciated. In fact, there is reason to believe that no possible decision policy for games against Nature can satisfy all the intuitive requirements that one can put on it. Luce and Raiffa (1957, Chapter 13) have developed an axiomatic statement of the criteria which an ideal decision policy for games against Nature ought to fill, and showed that these criteria contain contradictions. The topic is too complex to be dealt with at length here. Instead, we shall attempt to give the flavor of the problem, then propose an approximate solution.

To give an idea of what the nature of the problem is, we construct a hypothetical problem which might be faced by a user of CLS programs.[4] Imagine a research physician who is interested in determining what factors are individually sufficient and jointly necessary to result in bacterial infection following surgery. Every surgical patient can be categorized as "infected subsequent to surgery" or "not infected," corresponding to positive and negative instances. We further assume that there is a very large amount of data, many measurements on many cases. In all probability there will be no one cause of infection, and in many cases the key factor may be a complex logical combination of the presence or absence of certain features. In other words, we have a concept learning problem. Realizing this, the physician decides to use CLS programs to develop decision trees characterizing his data, by regarding the known data as a sample from which he will build a trial concept. (We disregard the advisability of holding some data out as a check on the reliability of the concept.) Now we can consider several cases in which the physician would want the most efficient computer program possible. In the simplest case, he might want to reduce computation time for sheer economy. Therefore, he would want to be able to use as small a sample as possible. But he must keep other considerations in mind. If the physician is both a researcher and a clinician, he may be making decisions (e.g., whether or not a person is a good risk for surgery) using his trial concept while he gathers the data. In this case it is obviously to his advantage to minimize the number of errors made during learning. For the same reason, and also if data are expensive to obtain, he may wish to develop the concept using a minimum sample.

With all these things in mind, our hypothetical doctor decides to use one of the four programs, CLS-1, CLS-6, CLS-7, or CLS-8. He turns to the results of Experiment VIII for guidance and he finds that if he could make the statement, "Problems and subproblems will be similar in form to problem I.2, and I am more interested in minimizing errors than sample size," then he should choose the CLS-1 program (see Figs. 5.5 and 5.6). If he substituted problem I.5 for problem I.2, then the choice would be CLS-8. The doctor will probably be loath to make any such statement. Things become even worse if we, as "CLS builders," try to impose a solution for him, since we must decide for him whether he should minimize errors or sample size. This problem could arise even if we knew the form of the answer. For example, in problem I.3 CLS-6 produced the fewest errors and CLS-8 the smallest sample size. Thus a general, "user independent" solution seems even harder to develop.

There are two frequently advocated solutions to the dilemma. One is to

[4] Although this is an example, it is based upon a real pattern recognition problem presented to us.

"minimax," which in this case means choosing the program which produces the smallest maximum loss in terms of errors and sample size. In Experiment VIII this would lead to a unique solution, since CLS-8, under what for it are the worst possible conditions, will be better than any other program under its worst possible conditions, whether we consider errors or sample size. But this is a special case of Experiment VIII, and cannot be relied upon in future experiments. If one program was a minimax criterion choice by one measure, and another program the choice by another measure, some rule for combining costs would have to be stated. Besides, there is a more basic objection. It can be proven that if one is playing a game against an opponent who is rational in the sense that his gain is equal to your loss, and all he seeks to do is maximize his gain, then the minimax choice is always the best strategy. [This is the famous minimax theorem of von Neumann and Morgenstern (1948); for detailed expositions see Luce and Raiffa, and also Rapoport (1960), where a less mathematical argument is presented.] It is *not* reasonable to assume that concept learning problems are games against a rational opponent. To make such an assumption is tantamount to saying that Nature is out to get you. In the particular example relating to postoperative infection, this would mean that the staphyloccocal bacteria had chosen its environment so that it would be maximally inconvenient to discover. Since we reject such reasoning, we lose the key step needed to show that the minimax choice is a rational one. This does not mean that the minimax choice should be rejected as a possible alternative, it does mean that we should not choose a program simply because it is the minimax choice.

A second conventional solution is to regard all possibilities as equally likely, thus choosing that program which has the lowest cost averaged over problems. Again, this could lead to trouble if two cost measures produced two different programs with lowest average cost. As before, there is a more basic objection. Stating that all problems have equal probability is really quite a strong statement, since it assigns exact probabilities to each problem. This is hardly what we mean when we say we are ignorant of the state of nature. "Equal probability" statements carry with them a very specific assumption about the state of nature, one we are not willing to make.[5]

---

[5] We would only want to maintain this reluctance in situations in which the CLS program was to be used to attack a few problems, or in situations in which, once committed to a CLS program, one could not change easily as new statistics became available. If one can readjust one's actions as more information becomes available, a wide range of situations will yield to the application of Bayesian statistics, in which a readjustment of one's *a priori* probabilities leads to rapid convergence toward the true values. Recently published theorems (cf. Edwards *et al.*, 1963) show that when such rapid convergence techniques are possible the assumption of initially equal probabilities does not lead to any great error in most cases.

We do propose to do something to evaluate the results of Experiment VIII. Further, the method we advocate is potentially applicable to any experiment in the artificial intelligence field which has the general form of trying out different programs to solve different problems. The proposal involves the assumption of a class of combination rules for cost measures, and some relaxation of the statement that we are "completely ignorant" of the state of nature. Instead we consider a situation in which the exact probabilities of encountering each problem are not known, but some limits can be put on these probabilities. To return to our example, the physician might be unwilling to assign probabilities to his encountering a problem of a particular type, but he might be willing to rank order the problems from most to least likely. Such situations seem to us to be fairly common. We now develop our approximate solution for them.

Assume that "Nature," an indifferent opponent, has selected one of I possible problems. We attempt to solve the problem by using one of J programs, and our success will be evaluated in terms of K different costs. Associated with each program-problem combination, are K different cost elements, (c_{ijk}), corresponding to the cost, measured by method k, of using program j to solve problem i. To make the situation concrete, consider the simple situation in which two programs may be used to evaluate a problem, the problem may be one of two types, and two costs, errors, and total sample size, are used to evaluate performance. Thus $I = J = K = 2$ in this example. A hypothetical table of costs is shown in Table 5.3. Notice that this particular problem has two minimax solutions, depending on which of the cost measures is considered more important.

TABLE 5.3
Cost Factors for Hypothetical Problem Used to Illustrate Selection by Approximation

	No. of errors of classification		Total no. of observations	
	Problem 1	Problem 2	Problem 1	Problem 2
Program 1	3	8	10	20
Program 2	9	2	15	5

We assume that associated with the ijkth combination of cost, program, and problem there is a disutility d_{ijk}, which is a linear function of the actual cost. That is,

6.1 $$d_{ijk} = a(c_{ijk}) + \gamma_k.$$

The variable γ_k plays the role of the minimum cost by this measure, and, as we shall see, drops out in later calculations. Although more sophisticated definitions are possible, the intuitive notion that "disutility is that which a rational man keeps at a minimum" will serve our purpose. (Alternatively, we could say that a rational man maximizes his utility.) Equation 6.1 amounts to the assumption that we can observe some measure linearly related to the (psychological) disutility the user will experience if he attacks a particular problem with a particular program, and is charged in accordance with the particular variable we are observing.

The user will want to minimize his expected disutility over all costs. But first, we consider the contribution of a particular cost to the expected disutility. This is determined by taking the average disutility of particular program-problem combinations, weighted by the (unknown) probabilities $\{P_i\}$ of encountering each problem. The contribution of a given cost to the disutility of using a certain program is

6.2
$$E(d_{.jk}) = \sum_i^I P_i[a_k(c_{ijk}) + \gamma_k]$$
$$= \sum_i^I P_ia_kc_{ijk} + \sum_i^I \gamma_kP_i$$

Since, from the definition of probability

6.3
$$\sum P_i = 1; \qquad P_i \geq 0$$

equation 6.2 becomes

6.4
$$E(d_{.jk}) = a_k \sum_i P_ic_{ijk} + \gamma_k$$

The expected total disutility of a program, however, will be a weighted sum of the contribution to disutility by each cost index. The weights $\{a_k\}$ may be used to determine this. Without loss of generality we may place on them the constraints

6.5
$$a_k \geq 0, \qquad \sum_K^K a_k = 1.$$

Then the expected disutility of the jth program, D_j, is given by

6.6
$$D_j = \sum_k a_k \sum_i P_ic_{ijk} + \sum a_k\gamma_k$$

Since $\sum a_k\gamma_k$ is a constant for all programs, we may disregard it. Although the weights, $\{a_k\}$, and the probabilities, $\{P_i\}$, are unknown, it is clear that if one program has the minimum expected disutility for all costs, considered separately, given a particular set of probabilities, then that program is optimal for that set of probabilities regardless of the weights of the costs. For any given set of probabilities it is thus possible to establish constraints which the weights must meet to make a particular program optimal. We can then ask whether these weights or probabilities are "reasonable" in a given situation without committing ourselves to an exact statement of their value.

We illustrate using the sample problem of Table 5.3. If Program 1 is optimal for each cost factor considered separately, then

6.7 (a) $$D_{11} < D_{21},$$

(b) $$3P_1 + 8P_2 < 9P_1 + 2P_2,$$

(c) $$P_2 < P_1,$$

and

6.8 (a) $$D_{12} < D_{22},$$

(b) $$10P_1 + 20P_2 < 15P_1 + 5P_2,$$

(c) $$3P_2 < P_1.$$

Since P_1 and P_2 must sum to unity, both equations 6.7 and 6.8 are satisfied if P_1 is greater than .75. Neither condition is satisfied if P_1 is less than .50. If P_1 is greater than .75, then Program 1 is optimal ($D_1 < D_2$). Similarly if P_1 is less than .50 Program 2 is always optimal. If $.50 \leq P_1 \leq .75$, then optimality depends on the specific value of a_k. It should now be clear why we say that the problem is partly solved. If we are willing to make some statement between complete ignorance and absolute knowledge of the probabilities, then, depending on that statement, the problem of selecting the correct program may be solved.

This criterion is only useful when (a) the disutility of a particular cost is a linear function of that cost and when (b) we are willing to place some restriction on the possible values of the various probabilities of encountering problems. The first assumption is a reasonable one, and was introduced in a straightforward manner. The second one came in by implication and it turns out that the first assumption is only a help when we are willing to make the second one. The second assumption temporizes with the axiom of complete ignorance. But are we ever in complete ignorance? It seems that the usual situation is one in which we are unwilling to state the exact probability of Nature's being in a particular state, but are willing to set some boundary limits on that probability.[6]

[6] Techniques exist for translating "reasonable verbal statements" of one's information about the probabilities into numerical statements (Abelson and Tukey, 1959). Discussing them here would carry us too far afield.

TABLE 5.4

CASES USED IN SOLUTION OF PROGRAM SELECTION PROBLEM
FOR PROBLEM SET I: EXPERIMENT VIII

Case	Probabilities of finding problem types				
	I.1	I.2	I.3	I.4	I.5
1	.2	.2	.2	.2	.2
2	.6	.1	.1	.1	.1
3	.1	.6	.1	.1	.1
4	.1	.1	.6	.1	.1
5	.1	.1	.1	.6	.1
6	.1	.1	.1	.1	.6
7	.25	.25	1/6	1/6	1/6
8	.25	1/6	.25	1/6	1/6
9	.25	1/6	1/6	.25	1/6
10	.25	1/6	1/6	1/6	.25
11	1/6	.25	.25	1/6	1/6
12	1/6	.25	1/6	.25	1/6
13	1/6	.25	1/6	1/6	.25
14	1/6	1/6	.25	.25	1/6
15	1/6	1/6	.25	1/6	.25
16	1/6	1/6	1/6	.25	.25

TABLE 5.5

OPTIMAL PROGRAM FOR EACH OF 16 CASES
CONSIDERED UNDER LINEARITY ASSUMPTION: EXPERIMENT VIII

Case	Optimal program by expected errors		Optimal program by expected sample size	
	Program	Errors	Program	Sample
1	CLS-8	5.20	CLS-8	27.76
2	CLS-8	4.00	CLS-7	29.96
3	CLS-1, 6	4.94	CLS-6	19.92
4	CLS-6	5.64	CLS-8	25.38
5	CLS-8	4.80	CLS-8	24.18
6	CLS-8	5.50	CLS-8	26.38
7	CLS-8	5.10	CLS-8	29.31
8	CLS-8	4.93	CLS-8	28.68
9	CLS-8	5.12	CLS-8	28.88
10	CLS-8	5.06	CLS-8	28.71
11	CLS-8	5.23	CLS-8	27.53
12	CLS-8	5.42	CLS-8	29.48
13	CLS-8	5.36	CLS-8	27.56
14	CLS-8	5.25	CLS-8	27.10
15	CLS-8	5.19	CLS-8	26.93
16	CLS-8	5.38	CLS-8	27.13

These methods can be utilized to select the best of the four programs considered in Experiment VIII, for any combination of the five problems of Problem Set I. To do so analytically, however, would involve more complicated mathematical techniques than it would be appropriate to explain here. This is especially true since we are interested in demonstrating a method, rather than choosing a CLS program for a particular job. As a demonstration of the method, 16 different assignments of probabilities to each of the five problems were investigated. The 16 cases were generated by (a) regarding all problems as equally likely, case 1; (b) regarding one problem type as making up 60% of the potential problems, the remaining 40% of the "sample space" being distributed equally among the other four problems, cases 2–6; and (c) regarding two problem types as occupying one half of the problem space and sharing it between them, while the remaining three problems share equally the other half of the problem space, cases 7–16. The 16 cases are enumerated in Table 5.4. In Table 5.5, the optimal program by each cost index is shown. In 13 of the cases CLS-8 is the optimal program by both cost indices, in two others it could be optimal or not, depending on the particular weight assigned to sample size or classification errors. In only one case is another program (CLS-6) clearly the optimal choice.

7. CLS-9. AN ATTEMPT TO COMBINE EFFECTS

Experiment VIII suggested that, of the systems studied so far, some variant of CLS-8 would provide a most efficient concept learner. The experiments with CLS-2 and CLS-3 also suggested that good performance could be obtained from a system with limited memory. Finally, we would like to consider CLS programs which develop "n-ary" trees, such as the one illustrated in Figure 5.4, instead of restricting our consideration solely to trees with binary test points. Accordingly, our final artificial-intelligence experiment was an attempt to combine all these features into a single program, CLS-9, to see if substantial improvement did result.[7]

For those interested in programming a CLS, certain technical features of the CLS-9 program are worth considering. The program was written in Algol, the internationally accepted, machine independent programming language (Naur et al., 1960, 1962). The actual program used in the experiment to be reported is given in Appendix C. This program works on a principle quite different from that of the IPL-V programs. The decision tree representing a concept is produced by row by row development of a

[7] Experiment IX was performed at the University of Sydney approximately one year after the other experiments were completed. It had been intended that several more experiments with multiple-branching decision trees be conducted. Unfortunately, delays in the delivery of computing equipment and supporting programs made this impossible.

right tree matrix, a formalism due to Iverson (1962). He has shown that if the nodes of a tree are numbered in the normal reading order, left to right and top to bottom (as we have done, for instance, in Fig. 1.1), then it is possible to construct a matrix in which the nth row corresponds to the nth node of the tree which the matrix represents. The technical details of how this is done can be recovered from the program in Appendix C. The point to note here is that by representing a tree as a right tree matrix we have a nonrecursive description of the general CLS paradigm. The program also shows that it is possible to define a CLS program using the restricted dynamic storage allocation facilities available in Algol, instead of relying on the more flexible but much more time consuming storage allocation techniques available in IPL-V. This further delimits "bits and pieces" of a CLS program.

There are two nonnegligible practical advantages in using an Algol program. By defining the CLS algorithm in Algol, we make CLS available in a well-known computing language rather than the more powerful but more abstruse Iverson language, which, so far as we know, has not been released as a standard programming language for any computer. Similarly, Algol notation is much more widely used than the specialized IPL-V notation. Although IPL-V programming systems do exist for many American computers, as well as for a few English and European machines, they are generally interpretive systems. Their use in an extensive experimental series leads to computing bills which, outside of the richer scientific centers, cannot be tolerated. By contrast, the program given in Appendix C is compatible with the English Electric Company's "Whetstone" (Randell and Russell, 1964) and "Kidsgrove" (Huxtable, 1964) Algol systems. After compilation using the Kidsgrove system, which is purposely designed to give a fast execution program at the expense of slow compilation, the program for CLS-9 runs approximately 30 times faster on the English Electric KDF-9 than do comparable IPL-V programs run on the IBM 7090 using the RAND IPL-V interpretive system available in 1962.[8]

---

[8] We acknowledge that this is an approximation, because the method of representing CLS procedures is different in the Algol program, and because the internal workings of the IBM 7090 and the English Electric KDF-9 are quite different. In any one comparison so many factors are different that it is impossible to say that a difference in speed is due to IPL-V, Algol, the machines, or the elegance of the programs. A good deal of experience has been gained by E. B. H. concerning the execution of both "artificial intelligence" and applied concept learning problems on both machines, using IPL-V, Algol, and machine-oriented programming languages. Similarly, P. J. S. has developed very much faster CLS systems for text analysis problems (see Chapter 8) using the machine-oriented FAP programming language for the IBM 7090. On the basis of this experience, we maintain that CLS programs written in an interpretive list processing

The Logic of CLS-9

CLS-9 is identical to CLS-2, the concept learning system with a limited, undifferentiated memory, except for its selection function. At each sub-problem (i.e., each interior node of the tree) CLS-9 uses as a test that attribute which will most aid in classifying items which have reached the node being examined. Specifically, let

7.1 $\mathbf{A} = \{\mathbf{A}_i\}$ = set of attributes not tested at any node above the current node;

     $\mathbf{K} = \{k\}$ = set of criterion classes (not necessarily limited to two as in previous programs);

     V_i = The number of possible values of attribute i;

     n_{ijk} = number of cases which are active at the current node, and have value j of attribute i and are in class k;

     $n_{ij}{}^*$ = maximum of $\{n_{ijk}\}$ over k.

CLS-9 determines all members of the set $\{n_{ijk}\}$, and for every attribute computes

7.2 $$H_i = \sum_{j=1}^{V_i} n_{ij}{}^*$$

The attribute which maximizes H_i is selected for testing. The program then sets up a node with as many branches below it as there are possible values of the selected attribute. The resulting tree is the "best possible" in the following sense: If one were to use the tree to classify all items in memory at the time the tree was constructed, obviously all these classifications would be correct. Further, if partial testing were to be carried out to some point above the endpoints of the tree, and the "most likely" classification given at that point, the decision procedure would maximize the number of correct classifications of the items in memory. Because of this, the logical argument for the CLS-9 procedure is very strong in cases in which memory is virtually infinite, since in such cases the procedure will maximize the number of correct classifications of all known cases if the decision tree is arbitrarily chopped short at any point. But is the argument equally convincing when only a limited memory is available? This question was asked in Experiment IX.

---

language run too slowly to be of use as regular production programs. This is not true of compiled or machine-coded CLS programs which are written without the use of list processing techniques. Whether adequate speed can be achieved by the use of a compiled program which contains list processing operations is not known.

EXPERIMENT IX

This experiment followed the format of the previous experiments. The problems of Problem Set I were used. A condition was defined as a combination of problem type and memory size. Within each condition, 10 samples of 100 items each were chosen, this time with replacement, stored in memory, and classified using the sequential procedure for classification and development of a new hypothesis following errors.

The sort of trial hypothesis CLS-9 could develop is different from the trial hypotheses developed by the previous programs in one important way. Since CLS-9 creates a multibranch tree, it may create endpoints for which there is no data in memory at the time the tree is developed. More specifically, suppose that at some point CLS-9 selects the ith attribute as its test at that node. The program will then create V_i branches from that node, corresponding to all possible outcomes of testing the ith attribute. For instance, if the attribute "size" is selected, allowance will be made for any category of size, even though the data in memory at the time may not include examples of all possible sizes of objects. As a result, the tree representing the trial concept will contain some endpoints which represent "nonexistent" data. The program can detect the logical possibility of encountering certain types of objects, but has no way of knowing how they should be classified when they are encountered. In the previous CLS programs all such cases were effectively lumped together in the "everything else" classification at the endpoint to the lower right of the decision tree. In CLS-9 the program has to allow for specific situations in which it cannot make a trial classification. Loosely, this is equivalent to a human concept learner's saying, "I can't even guess what this sort of item would be, although I admit that it is logically possible." When CLS-9 encounters an object that is routed to one of these "don't know" endpoints of its current tree, it treats it as an error in classification and a new decision tree is developed. Such errors were recorded separately from errors due to erroneous classification.

Tables 5.6 and 5.7 show, respectively, the number of errors during the learning phase and the accuracy of final answers under the different conditions of Experiment IX. Accuracy of final answer is expressed in terms of the "computation gain" (CG) score defined in Chapter 4, equation 2.1. For ease of comparison, the results achieved by CLS-2 in Experiment IV are also included. Other than the programs used, the only difference between Experiments IV and IX is that in the latter experiment the sample size was 100, with items selected with replacement from the universe of 256 possible objects, while in Experiment IV each sample contained 50 objects chosen without replacement from the same universe. The tables also show

TABLE 5.6

MEAN NUMBER OF TOTAL ERRORS AND ERRORS DUE TO FAILURE
TO CLASSIFY OBJECT IN EXPERIMENT IX, WITH COMPARISON
FIGURES FOR CLS-2 IN EXPERIMENT IV

Problem	Memory size	Errors (CLS-2)	Total errors (CLS-9)	Adjustments (CLS-9)
I.1	10	4.5	8.3	4.5
	20	3.9	4.0	2.4
	30	3.7	4.3	2.3
	100	—	6.6	3.9
I.2	10	6.7	26.1	9.3
	20	5.3	13.9	7.1
	30	5.2	10.5	6.2
	100	—	9.2	5.1
I.3	10	7.6	9.8	5.3
	20	5.1	5.8	2.8
	30	5.9	5.0	2.8
	100	—	5.0	2.7
I.4	10	13.1	36.0	14.5
	20	8.7	21.0	9.9
	30	7.4	14.2	6.3
	100	—	13.9	6.7
I.5	10	21.2	37.2	13.4
	20	19.6	17.2	8.5
	30	18.1	14.9	7.4
	100	—	12.4	5.9

TABLE 5.7

COMPARISON OF MEAN CG SCORES FOR CLS-2 AND CLS-9
AT DIFFERENT MEMORY SIZES

Problem	Program	Memory size		
		10	20	30
I.1	CLS-2	.14	.74	.81
	CLS-9	.49	.90	.90
I.2	CLS-2	1.00	1.00	1.00
	CLS-9	.35	.51	.76
I.3	CLS-2	.80	.83	.77
	CLS-9	.48	.97	.97
I.4	CLS-2	.60	.91	.95
	CLS-9	−.02	.91	.95
I.5	CLS-2	.00	.25	.44
	CLS-9	.05	.58	.61

the results of using CLS-9 with a memory size of 100. In Table 5.7 a distinction is made between CLS-9 total errors and errors due to the current trial concept's being inadequate to categorize an item at the time it is presented. These are listed as "adjustments."

The results obtained with CLS-9 are quite similar to those obtained previously. If we treat the experiment as a fully crossed, factorial design, "problems," "memory size," and the interaction between them are all significant effects at less than the .001 level using analysis-of-variance techniques. The pattern of effects at any one memory size is very similar to that obtained for CLS-8. The difficulty of a problem is related to the number of interior (test) nodes required to solve it, and there is no difference in difficulty between two problems with the same number of interior nodes. The level of performance achieved by CLS-9 appears to be equivalent to or somewhat below the level of performance achieved by CLS-2, both in terms of errors and accuracy of final answer. A discrepancy in favor of CLS-2 is particularly noticeable on problems I.2 (inclusive disjunction) and I.4 (exclusive disjunction).

That CLS-2 should be as, or more, accurate and less error prone than CLS-9 with a limited memory is somewhat surprising, especially since CLS-2 worked with a smaller sample. We maintain that CLS-9 provides the most economical "incomplete" tree for categorizing those objects which are in memory at the time the decision tree is developed. In developing its decision rules, CLS-9 does not accept the approximation, accepted by CLS-1 through CLS-8, of lumping together a group of heterogeneous items of the same criterion class into the "everything else" set routed to the lower right hand endpoint of the binary decision tree. This means that CLS-9 can run into difficulties on two distinct counts. First, the CLS-9 program must do much more computing, since it must examine the frequency distributions of values of each attribute over all classes of items. Compare this to the smaller amount of computing done by, say, CLS-8, which makes complete frequency counts of values of attributes only for the smallest criterion class in the set of objects it is examining. Second, CLS-9 will usually produce a tree with more interior (test) nodes than do the other programs. That is, it makes finer distinctions among its data. Since the total amount of data in memory is the same, a program which relies on finer distinctions is more likely to select a test which, owing to sampling fluctuations, is valid for the data in memory at the time but is not valid in the universe. Programs which, like CLS-1 through CLS-8, rely on grosser distinctions between types of objects are less likely to accept small, spurious correlations as indications to select particular attributes for testing in the decision tree.

Although this explanation seems a reasonable account of the failure of

CLS-9 to exceed the performance of the other programs, it is the result of *post hoc* reasoning. Some may find it suspect on that ground. Detailed examination of some of the item-by-item results from replications of different conditions of Experiment IX seems, subjectively, to be in accord with our reasoning.

8. DISCUSSION OF THE ARTIFICIAL INTELLIGENCE EXPERIMENTS

The general CLS paradigm does provide a way for writing workable concept learners, since the programs were capable of recognizing a complex logical pattern on the basis of experience with a relatively few objects. Whether the performance of the CLS programs is adequate is a rather harder question to answer. Adequate for what? In Chapter 6 some evidence is presented to indicate that CLS-1 does what it does in a more efficient manner than do people. This is a reasonable comparison, since it has sometimes been alleged that the unique advantage people have over machines is that people can, somehow, notice patterns in data. Others have shown that machines can do the same thing in the case of recognition of fairly simple patterns when objects are described in an imprecise way (e.g., the recognition of handwritten text). The work of Uhr and his associates (Uhr and Vossler, 1963, in particular) on a program for visual pattern recognition, and the work of Rosenblatt (1962) and others on perceptrons is a case in point. The CLS investigations show that a computer program can also be used to discover logically complex patterns in an environment in which the description of each object is precise and, by assumption, accurate.

The experimental results further indicate that improvement can be achieved within the basic CLS framework. In Chapter 4 it was shown that it is often possible to balance the memory requirements of a CLS system against the total amount of computing needed. A CLS system with a relatively small memory did very nearly as well as one with a perfect memory, although the nature of the program is such that the limited memory device requires fewer total computational steps to reach the same answer. There is, however, a complex balance between the amount of computation per error and the total number of errors that would have to be kept in mind in any situation in which the use of a CLS system with a limited memory was contemplated.

Within the limits of Problem Set I, it was shown that both the sample size and the number of errors of misclassification can be reduced by altering the subproblem selection routines of a CLS program. This is an encouraging sign, since the internal processes by which a concept learner analyzes data are always under his control. On the other hand, it is somewhat surprising how small the gains are when one uses a more sophisticated subproblem selection procedure. There is a clear change in the program's behavior if one changes from reliance upon the assumption, maintained in CLS-1 through CLS-5, that designation of objects as positive instances of a concept implies some common property or properties of those objects, to the symmetric treatment of positive and negative instances used by CLS-6 through CLS-9. Further alterations do not seem to help very much. In particular, CLS-6 and CLS-9 make considerably more calculations upon the available data than do CLS-7 and CLS-8, since the former two programs utilize the information available to them from the frequency distribution of values of attributes over all classes of objects, rather than the frequency distributions in one class only. However, the more complex programs do not give strikingly better performance.

One of our experimental results has seemed counter-intuitive to some of our colleagues. CLS-4 and CLS-5, the systems which contain mechanisms for selecting a sequence of observations which ought to be informative, did no better than CLS-1, which is an identical program except that it observes randomly selected instances. Why should this be so, and why is it counter-intuitive? We do not know, although we would like to offer some speculations. Before doing so, we wish it to be clear that we are saying that no *spectacular* improvement occurs when a selection mechanism is installed in CLS programs. Although CLS-4 and CLS-5 might, indeed, be somewhat superior concept learners to CLS-1, this superiority is not great enough to be detected in our experiments. Since these experiments were sufficiently sensitive to detect a fairly complex pattern of differences between other CLS programs, the claim that object selection does not make a great deal of difference seems a valid one.

It is possible that the "proper" sort of object selection would make a difference, but that in our programming of CLS-4 and CLS-5 we used weak methods. This challenge cannot be answered unless a specific alternative method is proposed. While we would encourage anyone who can think of a reasonable alternative to try it out, we ask that he bear in mind the constraint that the method must be executable before the learner knows either the form or content of the concept he is trying to discover. In our experience, this constraint rules out many techniques which, at first description, seem promising. The strategies executed by Bruner *et al.*'s (1956) subjects in their experiments on selection conditions in concept learning are among these.

A second challenge to our results is somewhat different, and is interesting because in considering it we have to consider why the experimental results seem unacceptable. The challenge is an argument by analogy to human concept learning. Practically everyone will agree that a scientist who plans a sequence of observations is more efficient than a haphazard observer.

Indeed, the ability to profit from planned observations can be demonstrated in a much more limited experimental setting (Hunt, 1965). Therefore, the argument runs, the fact that CLS programs do not benefit from control over their observations indicates either that there is a statistical aberration in our results or that we are dealing with a very crude sort of concept learning device.

We accept the second statement: this difference between CLS and human performance can be considered a deficiency in the system both as a model of human learning and as an artificial intelligence. But what sort of added complexity would give an artificial intelligence system an ability to profit from planned observation? Human problem solvers, especially efficient ones, seem to make a great deal of use of models of their world. A CLS program does this in a simple way when it builds a trial concept. This gives it a single model which can be tested by further observation. It has been argued that human beings may (and should) evaluate several plausible models, no one of which can be denied on the basis of present data. Planning a sequence of further observations, then, becomes a process of selecting those observations which will discriminate between the different models under consideration.[9] Since a CLS has only a single model of its environment, it cannot benefit from such a sequence of observations.

A second possible explanation for the difference between CLS performance and the allegedly more efficient performance of human subjects in this respect may be that the effectiveness of planned observations is closely related to the way in which memory is organized. In the experiments we conducted all programs had virtually unlimited access to all information that was ever presented. Since the total information in a sequence of observations was constant, the extent to which each item transmitted information was not terribly important. Thus the difference between performance with "information rich" and "information poor" sequences might not be as great as it would be if the space allotted for memory were to be restricted. The effect of controlling the information rate per observation would be even more accentuated if memory were to be organized in a hierarchial fashion, with those items which the system had marked as "informative" at the time they were entered into memory being located in easily accessible storage areas. It does not seem unreasonable to think of human memory as being such an information storage system.

Some areas for future investigation should be mentioned. We have

[9] The argument being made here is, loosely, the rationale behind Bayesian statistical decision making. The relation of Bayesian statistics to the interpretation of experimental evidence is discussed in a general paper by Anscombe (1964). A more detailed paper on evaluating experiments has been written by Edwards et al. (1963), while Hunt (1964a) and Watanabe (1960) have considered the problem of selecting observations.

already indicated that it would be advisable to include within CLS programs routines for computing either statistical or information-theoretic criteria to be used as a guide in subproblem selection. We have essentially no experience with such programs, although some work has been done on the question of when particular tests are appropriate for inclusion in a CLS program (Hunt, 1964b). Since this work has not yet been followed by experimental or completed analytical work, it is purposely omitted here. The development of a definition of the CLS procedure within the Algol language should aid greatly in writing the necessary programs.

The second area which needs a good deal of development is that of analytic study of CLS proposals. Virtually all of the evidence we present for and against different varieties of CLS programs is based upon Monte Carlo simulations of their performance in particular problem solving environments. Strictly speaking, all the results we describe are applicable only for the problems which have been investigated. Since problem structure is the largest single determinant of problem difficulty, this is a fairly severe restriction. After evaluating our results, one might feel justified in saying that CLS-8, as the program least sensitive to fluctuations in problem structure, would be a good choice as a concept learning procedure in an unknown problem environment. This is a reasonable interpretation of the evidence we have presented. In applications of concept learning programs to "real world" problems, we have relied on CLS-8 a good deal. But to what extent was our choice of this program dictated by the particular problems we chose in the Monte Carlo studies? We do not know. We need some theorems about the performance either of particular CLS programs or of CLS procedures in general, theorems which we can justify without appeal to experimental, and thus possibly invalid, results. In the absence of such theorems, however, it is necessary to guide our research by the results of Monte Carlo studies of problem solving.

Simulating Human Concept Learning

CHAPTER 6

Simulating Human Concept Learning.
Learning the Logical Connectives[1]

1. SIMULATING HUMAN CONCEPT LEARNING

The idea that a computer program can serve as a functional model of human thought has been developed in detail (especially Feldman, 1962; Newell and Simon, 1961a; Reitman, 1965). The person is looked upon as an active information processing device which receives signals from the environment, sorts them, and produces a second set of signals as output. A model describes a mechanism which, at the level of signal transmission, does the same thing. Suppose that, instead of trying to account for the behavior of a person, you were trying to guess what program was controlling a digital computer. One way to do this would be to feed numbers into the computer in some systematic way, and observe what came out. You could then sit down and try to write a program, perhaps for a different computer, which would produce the same input-output relations as those you had observed. Following this, you would have to verify your model of the hidden program by predicting what the computer would do with a new set of numbers. Replace the term "program" by "thought processes" and "computer" by "person" and the tactic of computer simulation has been described.

For us, the initial stages of observing consisted of a review of the literature on human concept learning. The excellent series of experiments by Bruner *et al.* (1956) were particularly relevant. They reported that successful problem solvers follow what they called "strategies," consistent methods for developing an answer. For instance, the "wholist strategy" for solving conjunctive concepts, which is included in all CLS programs, was first described by Bruner *et al.* as an abstraction of the performance of their subjects. Even more interesting for our purposes was an allegedly inefficient

[1] Portions of this chapter have appeared in a Working Paper, "The Development of Decision Trees in Concept Learning. II. Learning the Logical Connectives," by Earl Hunt and Janet Kreuter, Western Management Science Institute, University of California at Los Angeles.

strategy reported as characteristic of people's reaction to disjunctive problems in "real life." It is practically identical to the technique for defining subproblems used in CLS-1.

Based on the review, CLS-1 was written. This computer program produced the flavor, if not the details, of already conducted experiments. We felt that in concept learning there were, logically, two separate processes: the task of noticing what is relevant and the task of deciding how it is relevant. In the simple concept identification experiment (for example, learning that the class "GEK" consists of all red patterns) the second step is so trivial that it follows immediately from the first. We were more interested in precisely this second step.[2] Therefore our research concentrated on the learning of more complex concepts than have been used in most studies of human concept learning.

A second limitation on our investigations was that we wished to avoid the problem of providing a model of human memory. People may forget what they have been shown or, worse yet, they may remember it incorrectly. The various memory functions used with the different CLS programs represent only the crudest of models for this complex process. While construction of computer models of human memory should be possible, this is not our present task. We limited ourselves to experiments in which we could reasonably assume either that our subjects had a perfect memory (by access to a written record) or that the total amount of information presented was so small that they could remember it all.

In this chapter we report three studies in which university undergraduates tried to solve the five problems of Problem Set I in three different experimental settings. Their efforts were compared to the efforts of CLS-1 in comparable simulated conditions.

2. THE MATERIAL

The same general procedure was used to generate stimuli for all the experiments, so we shall describe it once in some detail. A subject would be presented with a sample of four-letter nonsense words constructed solely of consonants.[3] He was told which words were positive and negative instances and, at various points, was asked (a) to classify a new object or (b) to state his current hypothesis about the concept.

[2] After we had completed our work, a series of experiments by Haygood and Bourne (1965) was brought to our attention. These experiments were designed to separate the problem of learning which attributes are relevant (attribute learning) from the problem of learning how they are relevant (rule learning). That they were able to do this supports the usefulness of our distinction between noting what is relevant and how it is relevant. In general, the results of Haygood and Bourne are consistent with our own.

[3] By using consonants we avoided the problem of randomly creating English language words.

The positions of letters in the nonsense words, first letter, second letter, etc., corresponded to attributes, and the exact letter corresponded to the value of an attribute. To avoid confusions or the possibility of a response to relations between attributes, a particular letter never occurred in more than one position. In each experiment 16 consonants were chosen at random and, from these consonants, four were assigned to each attribute. For example, in one experiment W, Z, X, and N were assigned to the first place, G, P, J, and S to the second, M, V, H, and C to the third, and T, L, Q, and R to the last place. Thus in that experiment, WPHR was one of the words used, but PHRW was not.

The concepts of Problem Set I were used to form concepts about the nonsense words by equating two letters, in two different positions, with the relevant characteristics. Thus problem I.1 could be translated from its original form, "If value 1 of attribute 1 *and* value 2 of attribute 2 are present, the object is a positive instance," to the new form, "If the second letter is G *and* the third letter is M, the word is a positive instance." Note that a problem with the same logical structure could be formed by choosing different letters and positions, say C and R in the third and fourth places. This corresponds to the distinction between content and the structure of a concept, which was discussed in Chapter 2. There we pointed out that we were concerned only with the structure of concept learning problems, since CLS systems respond only to this. A similar restriction is not so easily placed on human beings. For instance, we found that concepts whose relevant attributes were contiguous positions (e.g., first and second position) were easier to learn than concepts based on spatially separated positions. Somewhat opposed to this, we also noticed that letters in the end positions of a word were easier to notice than the middle letters. Such variations in human performance are presumably due to perceptual preferences for which CLS has no counterpart. We wished to study other processes, and to wash out the "noise" due to content by our experimental design.

In order to determine what effects were due to content variation (in order to discount them) we constructed pairs of problems which were identical except for content. How this was done, and the relation between content and structure, is perhaps best understood by looking at the example in Table 6.1. This presents two problems which can both be given the structure, "Positive instances have value 1 of attribute 1 or value 1 of attribute 2." The difference between the two problems is (a) in the assignment of positions in the words to particular attributes and (b) in the selection of letters to represent values of those attributes. Thus for any word that is an allowable object in one problem there is a "rewriting rule" (the mapping ϕ given in the lower half of Table 6.1) which defines the corresponding object in the other problem. This makes it possible to define two

TABLE 6.1

AN EXAMPLE OF TWO PROBLEMS THAT ARE EXACTLY ALIKE
EXCEPT FOR THE CONTENT USED

Problem 1	Problem 2
Concepts	
G occurs in position 2 and	N occurs in position 1 and
M occurs in position 3	T occurs in position 4
Sequences	
WGMR – Positive	NPCT – Positive
XPCR – Negative	WJCL – Negative
ZPVL – Negative	WSVR – Negative
ZJHQ – Negative	ZGHQ – Negative
NSVT – Negative	XGMR – Negative
WJMT – Negative	ZPMT – Negative
XGML – Positive	NJVT – Positive

The mapping ϕ relating corresponding objects in each problem

$\phi(W) = P$	$\phi(G) = N$	$\phi(M) = T$	$\phi(T) = M$
$\phi(N) = G$	$\phi(P) = W$	$\phi(C) = L$	$\phi(L) = V$
$\phi(X) = J$	$\phi(J) = Z$	$\phi(H) = Q$	$\phi(Q) = H$
$\phi(Z) = S$	$\phi(S) = X$	$\phi(V) = R$	$\phi(R) = C$
ϕ (position 1)	ϕ (position 2)	ϕ (position 3)	ϕ (position 4)
= position 2	= position 1	= position 4	= position 3

samples, one for each problem, each of which transmits exactly as much information about the concept.

Two informationally equivalent samples can be chosen by first specifying the sample in terms of attributes and values, as was done in the artificial intelligence experiments, and then writing the nonsense words in accordance with the writing rules for that particular problem. From time to time we wished to observe the effects on concept learning due to the choice of informationally nonequivalent samples. This can be done simply by choosing two different samples, in terms of attributes and values, and then writing the nonsense words as appropriate. Varying samples in this way corresponds to the variation in sampling at each replication of a condition in the artificial intelligence studies.

The experiments themselves differed in the manner in which objects were presented and in the points at which the subjects were asked to state their hypotheses. In the first study words were presented one at a time, for the subject to classify as they occurred. A record of items presented was always available for the subject to inspect. In the second experiment all objects were presented at once. In the third experiment objects were presented in batches, the subject being required to sort each batch.

In general, the difficulty of a problem was measured by the number of erroneous classifications made. The three experiments were also simulated on the IBM 7090, using CLS-1 as a "subject." Its performance was compared to the averages over different contents for human subjects. By doing this, we obtained a measure of the amount of variation in the human learner's behavior associated with the form of the concept and the sequence of objects seen. A CLS model can be expected to predict this behavior. We may ask what the probability of a human error is at a particular point, given that the information processing model also made an error. To the extent that this figure is higher, averaged over content variations, than the probability of a human error at points at which the model did not make an error, we have evidence that the human and the system may incorporate similar heuristics.

We would always expect a CLS program to do somewhat better than people, since it is not subject to some of the sources of errors which plague human beings. Computer programs cannot misread words, be inattentive to instructions, develop inconsistent decision rules, or look for concepts based upon some idiosyncratic meaning of words or letters. We instructed our subjects not to do these things either, but naturally, these instructions did not always have their desired effect. The best we can hope to say is that our simulation is of the "rational thought" of the students who attacked these problems. What other psychological phenomenon they may have displayed during the experimental session, though it may have been quite interesting, is not our present concern.

3. EXPERIMENT X

This experiment was designed as a replication of Experiment I, with human subjects instead of CLS-1. Using the abstract definitions of attributes and values, two samples of 50 objects were selected by random sampling, and two different definitions of content (assignment of particular positions and letters as attributes and values) were stated. This provided us with four sets of 50 nonsense syllables, representing the four possible combinations of two samples and two types of content. From the point of view of the CLS program, however, there were only two different samples, since the program disregards content.

The five problems of Problem Set I were used. For each problem two values of different attributes were selected as relevant, and substituted in the appropriate form for that problem. Different attributes and values were used for each problem because we wished to use the same subjects on different problems, and did not wish them to learn that particular positions and letters were always relevant.

Forty students were recruited as subjects through the University of

California, Los Angeles (UCLA), student employment service. They were randomly divided into four groups of 10, corresponding to the four sets of five problems. Each subject was seen individually. He sat at a table on which were two cards, one marked with a plus sign and one with a minus sign. The experimenter, sitting across from the subject, had a deck of cards on each of which was printed one nonsense word. The cards were shown to the subject one at a time, and he was asked to predict whether the card would be placed under the plus sign or the minus sign. The experimenter then placed the card, face up, on the table under the correct symbol. Subjects were permitted to proceed at their own speed but were forced to respond to each nonsense word. Thus each subject at least had the opportunity of consulting a perfect record of all previously presented information. At the end of each problem, the subjects were asked to write down a statement of the correct concept. The order of problems within a set was chosen randomly for every subject.

Problems were constructed and presented to CLS-1 in exactly the same manner as in Experiment I.

RESULTS

The experimental design can be described as a mixed model involving crossing and nesting of variables (Scheffe, 1959, Section 8.2). Samples and contents were chosen at random and are fully crossed, every possible combination having been used. Subjects were also regarded as having been randomly selected from a larger population. Different subjects were used within each content-sequence combinations; hence subjects represent a random variable nested within content-sequence combinations. The problems were arbitrarily selected and are regarded as fixed. Since every subject attempted each type of problem with each content, the form variable is fully crossed with subjects, sequences, and contents.

The mean number of errors is plotted in Fig. 6.1. An analysis of variance is presented in Table 6.2. The significant effects are problem, content $\times$ problem interaction, and (marginally) problem $\times$ sample interaction. By far the greatest source of variation is due to the type of problem. The relative difficulty of problems was generally the same as with CLS-1, conjunctive problems (I.1) were relatively easy to learn, inclusive disjunction and implication next easiest (I.2, I.3), and exclusive disjunction and the biconditional (I.4, I.5) the most difficult.

The significant interaction terms can be explained by reasonable (although *post hoc*) analyses. The information content of a particular sequence of objects is not the same for different concepts, so a given sequence will favor the learning of one problem more than it will another. Over randomly chosen sequences this should average out. It may have done so

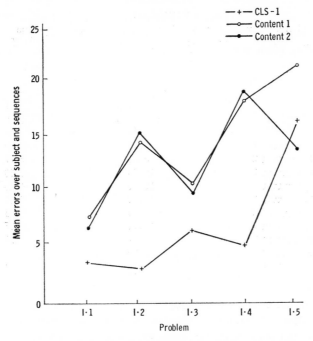

Fɪɢ. 6.1. Errors as a function of form and content. Experiment X.

here—the level of significance indicated in Table 6.2 is marginal. If significant, the effect does not seem to be large.

The content × problem interaction has been demonstrated much more reliably. Content effects are essentially "noise" in this experiment. They

TABLE 6.2
Aɴᴀʟʏsɪs ᴏғ Vᴀʀɪᴀɴᴄᴇ ᴏғ Eʀʀᴏʀs: Eхᴘᴇʀɪᴍᴇɴᴛ X

Sources	D.f.	mS	Error term	F
(1) Series (S)	1	72.00	$(3 + 5)^a$	<1
(2) Content (C)	1	1.28	$(3 + 6)^a$	<1
(3) Subj. (I)	36	31.60	None	—
(4) Problem (F)	4	1034.40	$(6)^c$	$17.86, p < .01$
(5) S × C	1	72.00	None	—
(6) S × P	4	57.92	$(8)^b$	$2.63, p < .10$
(7) C × P	4	140.43	$(8)^b$	$6.38, p < .01$
(8) I × P	144	22.02	None	—
(9) S × P × C	4	17.80	(8)	<1

[a] Pooled by rules given by Scheffe, 1959, Chapter 7.

[b] Substituted as stable estimate of (9).

[c] Most conservative estimate of error variance.

TABLE 6.3

COMPARISON OF ERRORS MADE AT DIFFERENT LOCATIONS
IN SIMULATION AND EXPERIMENTAL PHASES: EXPERIMENT X

Problem	Mean errors by subjects	
	Items where simulation makes error	Items where simulation is correct
I.1, Content 1	7.75	1.78
I.1, Content 2	8.33	2.77
I.2, Content 1	16.00	6.60
I.2, Content 2	10.50	4.43
I.3, Content 1	12.20	6.64
I.3, Content 2	14.20	7.58
I.4, Content 1	12.00	3.07
I.4, Content 2	8.67	3.41
I.5, Content 1	7.28	7.72
I.5, Content 2	10.62	4.98

represent the differential use of particular arbitrarily designated symbols and/or positions by human subjects. A significant content × problem interaction would be expected if biases toward looking at particular symbols or combinations of symbols (e.g., the first letter of a consonant cluster) are effective determiners of behavior only when the underlying form of the concept is quite difficult. Figure 6.1 demonstrates that this is the case. Content effects are marked only for the most difficult problem (I.5).

The significance of these results should be treated with some caution owing to statistical problems involved. While Bartlett's test for homogeneity of variance (Snedecor, 1956) is satisfied when computed on all treatments, this is because each form is replicated over contents and sequences. Within treatment, variance is a function of problems and is highly correlated with mean errors. Strictly speaking this invalidates the analysis of variance models. However, comparison of this case to similar examples (Scheffe, 1959, pp. 355–356) indicates that the F-test is approximately correct. We could increase our probability estimates considerably and still reach conventional levels of significance for the "problems" effect.

Because of these questions, the best we can do is make the rather unsatisfying statement that the difficulty of a particular problem may be determined, in part, by complex interactions between the content, sequence, and form of the concept to be learned. Our design is inadequate to evaluate this interaction precisely.

In Figure 6.1, the results obtained from CLS-1 and people are compared. On nine of the 10 problems based on form and sequence, CLS-1 did better.

This is not surprising; it was pointed out that CLS's are impervious to some types of errors which do affect human beings. What is more interesting is that in one type of problem, the biconditional, human beings do either as well as or better than CLS-1. People faced with the difficult biconditional problem, in which the class of positive instances includes all items that either contain both letters relevant to the concept or neither of them, seem to redefine the problem as one of finding a concept about negative instances. CLS-1 does not have this facility; it has been programmed to accept the experimenter's designation of positive instances as given. The program then conducts all of its heuristic searches on this set of objects, treating positive and negative instances in an asymmetric fashion. Also relative to the other problems, human subjects have much more difficulty with inclusive disjunction problems than does CLS-1. This suggests that systems which do have a "redefinition capability" would be better simulators, but time did not permit a test of this conjecture.

The behavior exhibited by human subjects may be compared to simulation behavior within as well as between problems. The frequency of errors made by human subjects on a particular item was higher for those items on which CLS-1 made errors than for items which CLS-1 identified correctly on all problems except for the biconditional (Table 6.3). There, knowledge of the response of CLS-1 is almost useless in predicting the responses of human subjects. This is further evidence that on the biconditional problems CLS-1 is a poor predictor of human performance.

4. EXPERIMENT XI

In some ways Experiment X is not a good test of the model. Although it is literally true that the previously presented objects were always available for inspection, there is some question as to whether the objects were "psychologically available." In the latter stages of the experiment upward of 40 cards were spread out on the table in front of the subject, and he may have balked at examining such an extensive record. Choice of objects at random, while it has some advantage, poses the problem that in some samples there may be a marked imbalance between positive and negative instances. While there always were both types of object in the sample, in some cases (especially problem I.1) positive instances were quite infrequent. For this reason, the simple "heuristic" of guessing that all objects are negative instances leads to only four or five classification errors. Similar, although not so dramatic, approximate answers can be obtained by such blind choice procedures in the other problems.

Experiment XI was an attempt to remedy these defects. Instead of presenting a large number of objects, one at a time, only a few objects were presented, and on a single trial. Instead of classifying objects as they were shown him, the subject examined the (small) sample given, then stated his trial concept in writing. The sample always contained eight positive and eight negative instances. The further restriction was placed that both positive and negative instances would exhibit exactly the same variation in irrelevant attributes. What this means can best be seen by looking at the sample problem (taken from those used in Experiment XI) which is illustrated in Fig. 6.2. The answer to this problem is "J in the second position and X in the third on all positive instances." The first positive instance, MJXS, has letters M and S in the two irrelevant places. There is a negative instance (MJCS) which also has M and S in the irrelevant positions. The other seven positive instances are similarly matched.

Figure 6.2 also illustrates a third feature of Experiment X, the negative instances are divided into two sets. This was done to imply to the subjects, without stating it, that the positive instances were somehow more closely

---

What is the "rule" used to assign "words" to class 2?

1.   MJCS, MJTK, MQXL, RQCS, RPTL

2.   MJXS, MJXL, ZJXS, RJXS, ZJXK, RJXL, RJXK, MJXK

3.   RQTK, ZPCS, ZPTK

FIG. 6.2. Example of stimulus used in Experiment XI.

connected to each other than the negative instances were. This is analogous to stating a "real life" concept learning problem as "dogs vs. rabbits, cats, pigs, . . ." rather than "dogs, vs. not dogs."

Under this procedure classification errors could not be recorded. Instead, subjects were timed by stop watch from the moment they were handed a card (similar to Fig. 6.2) with a problem on it until they stated that they were ready to write down an answer. Shepard *et al.* (1961), using a similar concept learning task, report that mean time to solve a problem and errors during learning are very highly correlated.

Ten UCLA undergraduates served as subjects. For each problem of Problem Set I, one sample of eight positive and eight negative instances was chosen and represented by two different contents, thus providing 10 problems. Each subject attacked each problem. A different random order was used for each subject, with the restriction that every person begin on a different problem.

RESULTS

Mean solution times are presented graphically in Fig. 6.3; Table 6.4 is the corresponding analysis of variance. A logarithmic transformation was used to normalize scores. The major source of variance is problem type,

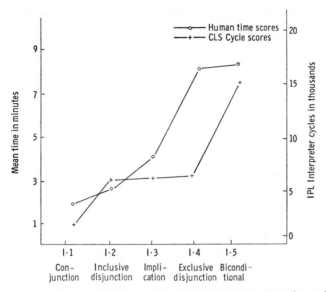

Fɪɢ. 6.3. Mean time to solution as a function of problems. Experiment XI.

although content does appear to exert some effect. (Note that content is a form of replication in the statistical model of this experiment, and cannot be tested directly.) The order of difficulty of problem types is much the same as was displayed in Experiment X, with fairly small differences between the two three-node problems, exclusive disjunction and biconditional.

TABLE 6.4

Aɴᴀʟʏsɪs ᴏꜰ Vᴀʀɪᴀɴᴄᴇ ᴏꜰ Lᴏɢᴀʀɪᴛʜᴍɪᴄ Tɪᴍᴇ Sᴄᴏʀᴇs: Exᴘᴇʀɪᴍᴇɴᴛ XI

Source	D.f.	mS	F
Problems	4	1.80	20.00
Subjects	9	.26	2.89
Interaction	36	.09	1.125
Repetition (content)	50	.08	—

Figure 6.3 also plots, on a separate scale, the number of IPL-V interpreter cycles used by CLS-1 when it attacks these problems. The same rank order between problems holds for human and program data, but there is no correlation between the differences between pairs of problems as measured by interpreter cycles and by time scores. In fact, the largest difference between pairs of problems is, for CLS-1, the exclusive disjunction–biconditional difference. This is the smallest difference for human subjects, a discrepancy between simulation and experiment that was also found in Experiment X. Again, this suggests that CLS-7, CLS-8, or CLS-9 would

provide a better simulation. Actually, any correspondence between cycles and time scores is encouraging, as the number of interpreter cycles used is only a very rough measure of the amount of computing effort expended by a program. The interpretation of time scores is similarly vague. The time a man spends on a problem is far from a perfect indication of the amount of "mental effort" he expends on it.

The subjects' statements of their categorizing rules were often difficult to interpret, especially for the more difficult problems. Practically every rule they offered could, with a fairly liberal interpretation, be interpreted as a decision rule adequate to categorize correctly the items on the card they were shown. Since many subjective factors entered into interpretation of the written statements, no further analysis was made.

5. EXPERIMENT XII

This experiment also attempted to minimize the role of memory in human concept learning. Four variations of Problem Set I, representing combinations of two variations of sample and two of content, were created as before. There were two major differences from the other two problems. The most immediately apparent was that the "sample" for each problem actually consisted of a *sequence* of 10 independently chosen samples of 10 items each. These small samples were presented all together, so that on a given trial the subject saw, and was required to classify, 10 objects instead of just one. Within a sample, items were chosen randomly with the restriction that the probability of choosing a positive instance was kept constant at .5, so that the number of positive instances in each sample varied randomly about a mean of five. Individual items were never repeated within the same sample, but might appear in different samples in the same sequence.

In simulating this task CLS-1 observed the correct classification of the first sample, then attempted to classify the second using the trial concept developed from the first. If all 10 classifications were successful, the program moved on to the next sample, continuing until an error was encountered. Following an error, a new trial hypothesis was developed, based only on the information contained in the current sample. The process then began again, continuing until 10 samples had been shown.

In the simulation five sequences were used. Two of these, the one hardest for CLS-1 and the one easiest for it (averaged over problems) were used in the experiment. Call these sequences SH (hard) and SE (easy). On four of the five problems CLS-1 solved the SE problem before the corresponding SH problem, on the fifth (problem I.2, inclusive disjunction) CLS-1 solved the problem on the first sample in both sequences. The two sequences were combined with two content codings (1,2) to create four sets of five problems, sets SE-1, SE-2, SH-1 ,and SH-2, for use with people. Twenty UCLA students served as subjects, five people attacking the problem set in each of the four sequence-content conditions.

The problems were presented to subjects on a TMI-Grolier "Minmax II" teaching machine, which is essentially a box with a crank and viewing window. The subject turned the crank until a sample of 10 items came into view. He circled those items he thought were positive instances, and then turned the crank until a new copy of the sample, showing the correct classifications, was in view. The subject viewed these for as long as he liked, then turned the crank until the next sample was in the window. Only correctly marked items were shown on the first sample.

RESULTS

The results for the human subjects and the CLS-1 simulation are shown in Fig. 6.4 and Table 6.5. For people, the order of difficulty of problems is

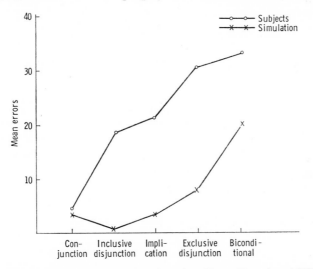

FIG. 6.4. Mean errors as a function of problems. Experiment XII.

the same as in Experiments X and XI. On each sequence there is a rough similarity between the experimental and simulation data, but three major discrepancies stand out. CLS-1 makes fewer errors, especially on the inclusive disjunction problems. As in the previous experiments, CLS-1 does not equate the exclusive disjunction and the biconditional problems, while human subjects do.

Table 6.6 summarizes the accuracy with which CLS-1 predicts subjects' responses. While 77% of the subjects' responses are predicted by CLS-1 (i.e., if a subject and an item are selected at random, chances are 77 out of

TABLE 6.5

ANALYSIS OF VARIANCE OF TOTAL ERRORS: EXPERIMENT XII

Source	D.f.	mS	Error term	F
(1) Series (S)	1	2007.04	(3 + 5)	—
(2) Contents (C)	1	556.44	(3 + 5)	—
(3) Subjects (I)	16	332.30	None	—
(4) Problems (P)	4	2507.15	6–9, pooled	26.90[a]
(5) S × C	1	1584.04	None	—
(6) S × P	4	73.54	8–9, pooled	—
(7) C × P	4	41.09	8–9, pooled	—
(8) I × P	64	96.71	None	—
(9) S × C × P	4	108.74	8	—

[a] $p = .01$.

100 that that subject will have made the same response to that item as did the CLS), this is in part a spurious comparison. Eventually, CLS-1 solves every problem except the biconditional problem in the SH sequences. Most subjects also solve most problems, and when CLS-1 and a subject have both solved a problem their further responses will, of course, agree. A more sensitive indication is provided in the right hand section of Table 6.6,

TABLE 6.6

ACCURACY OF PREDICTION OF RESPONSE BY SIMULATION AND BY RANDOMLY CHOSEN SUBJECTS IN EACH GROUP: EXPERIMENT XII

Problem[b]	Fraction of responses predicted over all trials		Fraction of responses predicted correctly before solution[a]	
	By simulation	By subjects	By simulation	By randomly chosen subject
Conjunction	.93	.83	.78(200)	.55
Inclusive disjunction	.80	.61	[c]	.60
Exclusive disjunction	.67	.58	.64(128)[d]	.58
Implication	.76	.64	.81(610)	.61
Biconditional	.68	.53	.61(860)	.62
Mean	.77	.64	.70(1870)	.59

[a] Before solution is reached by predictor or predicted problem solver, using a criterion of two correct samples. The figure in parentheses is total number of responses being predicted.

[b] Aggregated over series and contents.

[c] No prediction. CLS solves problem at first sequence.

[d] Prediction for series SH only, CLS solves series SE on first trial.

where the accuracy of prediction of response is calculated only for those samples prior to the first two samples in which either the CLS or the human subject categorized all items correctly. Since the number of responses which can be compared varied from subject to subject and from problem to problem, the reliability of the comparison of CLS's and human beings differs in each situation. A total of 1870 responses (aggregated over problems) could be compared and of these 70% were correctly predicted by CLS-1—clearly a statistically significant figure.

A statement that a model's predictive ability is significantly greater than chance is the weakest positive statement possible. An alternate procedure is to ask if the simulation is a better predictor than a randomly chosen subject. This is essentially a statistical version of "Turing's test" (Turing, 1950): Can we tell whether we are looking at the responses of a man or a machine? Within each group, one subject was selected as a predictor, and his responses were used to predict those of the other subjects. This was done both for all responses and for all responses prior to the first perfect classification of a sample by either the predictor or the "predictee" subject. The results are shown in Table 6.6. The randomly chosen subject in each group is no more accurate a predictor of his fellows' responses than is the program. An illustrative interpretation of this remark is that if you wished to predict the responses of a randomly chosen subject and, as a hint, could be told either the responses of CLS-1 or of another randomly chosen subject, you would do better to observe the program. Within the limits of the experiment, then, CLS-1 passed Turing's test. You could not tell, from the record, whether you were seeing the responses of a man or a machine.

6. RELATION TO OTHER PSYCHOLOGICAL STUDIES

We wish to relate these results to an information processing model of human concept learning. However, we shall defer discussing this point until later. Here we make a minor digression, and discuss the results as they relate to other studies of human concept learning. In doing so, the fact that the studies were motivated by the work on CLS programs is, strictly speaking, irrelevant. Within an entirely psychological framework, we may speak of the relationship between the logical form of a concept learning problem and the difficulty human beings have in solving it.

Most studies of concept learning have used problems with an extremely simple form. Our experiments indicate that university undergraduates are capable of handling more complex problems in an experimental setting, although increasing the complexity of the tree form required to describe the classifying rule markedly increased the difficulty of the problem. Tangentially related studies indicated that this would be true. Bruner *et al.* (1956), reported that their subjects often utilized inappropriate strategies (i.e., strategies which were not algorithms, or which, though algorithms, placed heavy loads on memory) when solving disjunctive problems, while the strategies observed in concept learning problems were, in the main, efficient ones. Hunt and Hovland (1960) presented a sample of items that could be classified by either a conjunctive or disjunctive rule. On subsequent testing, they showed that their subjects had learned the conjunctive, but not the disjunctive, concept.

Neither of these studies directly compared disjunctive to conjunctive concept learning. That of Shepard et al. (1961) did. They used objects described by three two-valued attributes, and presented all possible classifications of four positive and four negative objects. The difficulty of their problems was related to the complexity of the tree form of the classification rule to be learned. In somewhat different terminology, Garner (1962) pointed out that in this study problem difficulty related to the extent which the classification rule had to be expressed by stating combinations of attributes and values, rather than stating the value of one attribute without regard to the value of others. He has related this to multivariate information transmission, and more particularly to his concept of the "structure" of transmitted information, which is similar to the idea of representing a concept as a tree structure. A program which was the precursor of CLS-1 was able to simulate the results of the Shepard et al. experiments (Hunt and Hovland, 1961).

A further direct test of the difficulty of learning concepts of varying complexity was provided by Wells (1963). Two of his results are of interest. One phase of Wells' study confirmed Hunt and Hovland's (1960) results by a somewhat different technique, and in a second phase Wells showed that exclusive-disjunctive concepts were harder to learn than inclusive disjunctions. This, of course, provided a direct contrast between problems requiring two and three nodes in the decision tree.

Neisser and Weene (1962) performed experiments which were complementary and confirmatory to our results. They also explicitly studied the effect of tree structure upon concept learning, and the objects which they used were also nonsense syllables which, although constructed by somewhat different rules than ours, can be described in terms of attributes and values. Ten different problems were used in their experiment, including the five of Problem Set I. Their results and ours are almost identical. The major differences are (a) that their subjects saw two types of each problem with slight evidence of a change in pattern of difficulty from the first to the second repetition and (b) that in their study the biconditional problem was always more difficult than the exclusive disjunction, which is even more in line with the simulation than our own results are.

The Neisser and Weene report also extended our results by an artificial intelligence investigation. In order to check on the possibility that the order of difficulty of learning complex problems might be due to differential information transmission, i.e., to see whether, for some complex combinatorial reason, a greater number of instances must be presented before all hypotheses except one are logically eliminated in the more complex problems, they programmed a computer to solve concept learning problems "by rote." Their program began with a record of all possible concepts and the associated denotations, and "learned" by eliminating one of the concepts from this bank every time an instance shown to it was a counterexample of the concept until only one concept remained. Hovland (1952) pointed out that this is a maximally efficient concept learner from a logical viewpoint, in the sense that it used every bit of information given it. On the other hand, it is woefully inefficient from a practical point of view, the memory bank must be larger than the largest conceivable computer if the problem involves objects only slightly more complex than Neisser and Weene's (cf. Kochen, 1961a). However, if their program reflected, in its performance, the difficulty in concept learning which we have attributed to our subjects and our simulations, this would be an indication that the difference between problems was not produced by the interaction between structure and problem solving process (human or CLS), but rather that it was produced simply by a lack of sufficient information to define the concept in the more complex problems. This is not the case. Neisser and Weene even report (p. 644) that the "memory bank" program takes slightly longer to define uniquely the simple trees than it does complex ones. They conclude that the order of difficulty of problems "seems to reflect hierarchical organization of conceptual processes in the subjects themselves" (p. 645). We concur.

A word of caution is in order. A good deal of evidence has been accumulated recently to indicate that when people know the form of the concept, so that all they must learn is what attributes are relevant, then concept learning can be described by an "all or none" model in which the subject suddenly achieves the correct answer. (See particularly the studies by Bower and Trabasso, 1963a,b.) These studies have been of the learning of simple "one dimensional" concepts (e.g., "All GEKS are red"), or of conjunctive concepts involving only two dimensions. In either case a simple tree is involved. It may be that if the subject is familiar with the more complex tree being used the one trial model will still hold. The evidence for this, although far from complete, should be mentioned. As one of the conditions of the Shepard *et al.* experiments, subjects repeatedly learned different concepts of varying form. Thus they acquired experience with the more complex concepts. As the experiment progressed the initially most difficult, most complex, concept (which involved a three-node tree) became easy to learn. There are two ways in which this could have happened. The subjects might have learned to recognize the form of a concept quite early in the problem, then attempted to fit attributes and values into this form in some all-or-none fashion. A second possibility, which Shepard *et al.* appear to favor, is that the subjects learned to describe the stimuli in a way which recast the form of the concept to a simple one.

Evidence favoring the first alternative has been offered by Kepros and Bourne (1963). They compared conjunctive and biconditional problems, finding very little difference in difficulty between the two. In particular, they found that increasing the number of irrelevant dimensions had similar effects on the two problems, something that would not be true in a CLS simulation (see Chapter 2). However, as they point out, they took great care to explain the form of a biconditional solution to their subjects before the experiment began. If, as we have suggested, subjects who "have the idea" of a particular solution use the same methods to discover what is relevant in a problem, already knowing how it must be relevant, then there are quite important differences between studies in which subjects must find the form of the concept and studies in which they must find how a particular form fits the problem at hand.

One can point to evidence against this argument. In Experiment XI we repeated types of problems, as did Neisser and Weene, and obtained no differences on first and second repetition. Similarly, Neisser and Weene evidently did explain the form of different concepts to their subjects, although their report is not very detailed on this point. There is insufficient evidence to decide the question. What is needed is a series of experiments in which the same subjects solve a series of different problems with similar complex form so that the effect of interproblem transfer on the strategies used in concept learning can be examined. Wells' report of changes in a "set" to look for conjunctive or disjunctive answers indicates that some changes do occur (cf. the discussion by Hunt, 1962, pp. 178–181) but not enough is known about their nature.[3]

In our experiments the subjects seemed quite ready to disregard the labeling of stimuli as "positive" and "negative" instances, especially with the more difficult concepts. This is somewhat at variance with previous results, in particular those of Braley (1962). He compared the difficulty of learning a concept which could be expressed as either a conjunctive concept describing positive instances or a disjunctive one describing negative instances to a problem in which the labels "positive" and "negative"

---

[3] Haygood and Bourne (1965) present some more detailed experimental evidence concerning this point. They suggest that the tree form of a concept is most closely related to difficulty when the form of a concept is to be discovered, but is less important when the form is known.

were switched. The first problem was significantly easier to learn. It may be that this "preference for positive definitions" disappears when people are faced with very difficult problems, such as the exclusive disjunction and biconditional definitions of a concept. Again, insufficient evidence is available at the present time.

Finally, we stress the wide range of individual differences which we found in these experiments. Especially on the more complex problems, we doubt if any two of our subjects proceeded in exactly the same way. This is an important fact, and ought not to be pushed out of the way as "error variance." Having two people solve the same problem provides a replication only in the most gross sense—the procedure might be justified on statistical grounds. While it is true that our program passed Turing's test, this is partly because people are so different that you cannot predict one's action from another's. Logically our data provides a picture somewhat akin to that obtained in factor-analytic studies. A single "general factor," call it CLS-like performance, accounts for most of the data. There is a significant amount left over, and we suspect that no single model will do much better in trying to produce a more accurate prediction. When Bruner, Goodnow, and Austin constructed *post hoc* descriptions of the strategies their subjects had used, which here would be analogous to writing a CLS program after observing how the subjects had responded to the various problems, they found it necessary to state several different strategies to summarize the performance of a fairly small number of subjects on problems of a single logical type. They also noticed that within a subject there would be variation in the strategy used from problem to problem. Both their results and ours suggest that in a complex mental task, such as concept learning, there is very little chance of producing a general model of human behavior which will be accurate in specific cases. A truly adequate model must take into account individual differences in styles of learning. This is not entirely a counsel of despair, since there will certainly be fewer models than people. We do suggest that there are major classes of learners, and that the laws describing their behavior may be qualitatively different. We shall present, in Chapter 7, some evidence which suggests that the type of strategy used may be related to academic achievement.

The Random Categorization Task[1]

1. RESPONDING TO RANDOM CATEGORIZATION

Any sample which does not exhaust the universe from which it is drawn permits more than one consistent concept to be inferred from it. Suppose a particular rule correctly categorizes every member of a sample which contains all but one of the objects in the universe. Is the missing object classifiable by this rule or is it an exception? In Chapter 1 we pointed out that although there is no certain way to answer the question, it is usually reasonable to place some sort of criterion of simplicity or low cost on a rule, and then to speak of the best rule which can be inferred from the data.

The problems of Problem Set I can be solved this way since they all have a "reasonable answer." This makes them useful problems to investigate in studying artificial intelligence systems, but it poses something of a problem when a program is to be used to simulate human reasoning. Two different problem solving strategies might produce the same answer not because they were equivalent in general, but because they both worked reasonably well. A somewhat more stringent test is to ask that both people and the CLS-1 program attempt to solve a problem to which there is either no answer or a very large number of reasonable answers. If the program and the people choose the same or similar answers out of a set of allowable ones, this will be further evidence in support of the simulation, adding to the observation that, in precisely defined situations, people and programs have about the same amount of trouble reaching a solution.

To do this, we need a task in which people are known to be fairly consistent, though irrational, in their choice of solutions. Some tangential evidence in the literature suggested that the problem of finding a concept to explain a completely arbitrary classification was such a task. [This literature, which we discuss only by reference to papers on stochastic

[1] Portions of this chapter appeared previously in a Working Paper, "The Development of Decision Trees in Concept Learning. III. The Random Categorizing Task," by Earl Hunt and Janet Kreuter, Western Management Science Institute, University of California at Los Angeles.

models (Atkinson and Estes, 1963) and to computer simulation of the strategies involved (Feldman, 1962) is principally concerned with the behavior of people trying to guess the next item in a random sequence of ones and zeros.] People seem to be unable to accept the idea of a random situation. Instead, they try to read order into random data. The particular order which they assume may be determined by their responses to new stimuli. A CLS program would always develop some categorizing rule for any arbitrary learning sequence. Would people find the same rule? This is the question we asked in the next experiment.

2. EXPERIMENT XIII

A universe of 256 four-letter nonsense syllables was defined in the same manner as in the previous three experiments, by assigning letters and positions as values and attributes. To create a problem, 12 syllables were selected, randomly, and were randomly divided into subsets of six positive and six negative instances. We then selected 12 new syllables, again at random, from the remaining 244 possible objects. The subject would be shown the arbitrary categorization of the first 12 syllables, and then asked to "use the same rule" to divide the next 12 into positive and negative instances. An exactly analogous task was presented to CLS-1, using purely symbolic material.

Fifteen such problems were constructed. The first sample of 12 objects in each problem will be referred to as the training set, the second 12 as the test set. The training set was divided, as indicated, into six positive and six negative instances. The positive instances were typed on one line of a 3 × 5 in. file card, and the negative instances on the other two lines. As in Experiment X, this was done to suggest that positive instances were grouped together for some sensible reason. Each line had a plus sign, an asterisk, or an ampersand in front of it to identify the line to the subject. The test set nonsense syllables were typed on a separate card of the same size but different color. Thus every problem required two cards. The same order of problems was used for every subject. As an example, the cards from problem 1 are shown in Fig. 7.1.

From casual conversation with subjects in the previous experiment, we began to suspect that differences in the concept learning strategies used might be correlated with academic background. It is not unreasonable to suppose that one's style of inductive thought may be influenced by training in such diverse topics as theatre art and mathematical logic. We decided to gather some data on this by purposely using a heterogeneous group of subjects. Seven seniors or graduate students were recruited from a course in mathematical logic (group L) and seven from a course in Greek history (group H). Five freshmen or sophomores were recruited from the UCLA

First card

* Z J H Q,	X S M T,	Z J H L,	Z P M R,	N G H Q,	X S M L
+ Z G H T,	N P V T				
& X J C L,	N P H Q,	N J C Q,	X J C R		

Second card

Which of these items should be in the line marked * in the previous card?
    Circle them.

W G H T,   Z P V Q,   Z P H L,   W P H Q,   W G H R,   W J C Q

X P M R,   Z S V Q,   X S H Q,   N J H R,   X J H T,   X J V L

Fig. 7.1. A sample problem. Experiment XIII.

"gifted student" program (group G), and eight freshmen or sophomores (group P) from the introductory psychology class.[2]

EXPERIMENTAL PROCEDURE

Subjects were seen in groups of five or less. At the beginning of the experiment the concept learning task was explained in detail, using the following guide:

Suppose you were training to replace a man in a post office. This man's job is to sort letters into one of three bins. For some reason he will not speak to you. You must learn how to sort mail by observing the symbols on the envelopes that he puts into each bin. At some point you will have to replace him, and decide how to sort envelopes you have never seen before.

In this experiment you will do something very much like this. In front of you is a deck of alternating white and yellow cards. The yellow cards contain three lines of nonsense words. One line always has six words, the other lines have less than six words. Study the yellow card until you think you know what rule was used to place the words into the longest line on the card. The rule will always be based on the letters in the words, and not on anything else. For instance, the rule will not be based on the pronunciation of the words, the position of letters in the alphabet, or the fact that some of them might have meaning to you. When you are satisfied that you know

[2] Two subjects were found to be juniors who had signed up for the experiment by mistake. One subject either misunderstood or ignored the instructions. Each person was in a different group. Interestingly, one of the juniors, although she had signed up through the psychology class, was actually a physical science major who was taking a lower division course to fulfill administrative requirements. Her scores were quite typical of the students in the mathematical logic class. The question is, of course, is she "really" a psychology student or was she more like the logic students? We resolved the problem by not including her score in the reported statistics. If her score is included none of the differences between groups have their significance level changed.

what the rule is, place the yellow card face down in front of you. Do not look at it again. You will then see a white card containing twelve new words. Circle those you think belong in the same group as those on the longest line of the yellow card. Then place the white card face down in front of you.

The next yellow card will present a new problem. Continue working at your own speed until you are through. Some of the problems may seem difficult. Remember, you are not being timed and may take as long as you wish. Please do not talk during the experiment.

The subjects were permitted to ask questions. These were answered by paraphrasing the initial instructions.

RESULTS

Each subject designated 179 objects as positive or negative instances.[3] In the simulation phase 74 of the test objects (41%) were designated as positive instances by CLS-1. These will be referred to as predicted positive instances. Table 7.1 summarizes the distribution of the subjects' responses to the predicted positive and predicted negative instances. The subjects

TABLE 7.1

ASSOCIATION BETWEEN SIMULATION PREDICTIONS AND SUBJECTS'
CHOICES OF POSITIVE AND NEGATIVE INSTANCES: EXPERIMENT XIII

Selection	Predicted positives	Predicted negatives[a]	Totals
Selection of items as positives	911	781	1692
Selection of items as negatives	1087	2054	3141

[a] Contingency test for significance of association: all subjects, $\chi^2 = 168$, $p < .01$; group L, $\chi^2 = 13.16$, $p < .01$; group H, $\chi^2 = 9.39$, $p < .01$; group G, $\chi^2 = 4.00$, $p < .05$; group P, $\chi^2 = 3.79$, $p < .10$.

called an average of 35% of the objects positive, and selected more of the predicted positives as positive instances than predicted negatives. This trend is statistically significant at better than the .01 level using the chi-square test for contingency (Snedecor, 1956). The same test, applied to the relation between predicted and obtained responses of individual subjects, provided chi-square values of from 1.07 to 21.98, each on 1 degree of freedom. Of the 27 possible chi-square tests 16 exceeded the .05 level of significance and 21 exceeded the .10 level. All comparisons were in the direction of more agreement between model and subject than would be expected by chance. If the subjects are grouped by sources (L, H, G, and P) chi-square values are significant at .10 or better for each group (see Table 7.1).

The fact that the chi-square values for the comparison to the model

[3] One item was mistyped.

differ for different groups suggests that the accuracy of the simulation varies with academic background. Table 7.2 summarizes the relevant data. A predictability score for each subject was defined by determining the coefficient of contingency between his responses and the responses of CLS-1. Group L contained the most predictable subjects, followed in order by groups H, G, and P.

TABLE 7.2

ASSOCIATION BETWEEN PREDICTABILITY OF RESPONSE PATTERNS
AND SUBJECTS' ACADEMIC BACKGROUNDS: EXPERIMENT XIII

Subjects by quartiles in order of predictability	Subjects by academic background[a,b]			
	Logic (L)	History (H)	Gifted (G)	Psychology (P)
I (Most predictable)	5	2	0	0
II	2	2	1	2
III	0	2	4	1
IV (Least predictable)	0	1	0	5
Distribution of subsets	7	7	5	8

[a] Over-all association: $\chi_9^2 = 25.82$; $p < .01$.
[b] Association by pairs of groups (exact probabilities): L vs. H, $p = .13$; H vs. G, $p = .12$; G vs. P, $p = .02$.

Comparing the CLS-1 program to chance prediction is a doubtful procedure, since no one seriously believes that chance is a very good model anyway. A more meaningful comparison is to match the CLS-1 predictions against either the best possible predictions that could be made by any general model or against other models which seem intuitively reasonable.

First, consider how much prediction is possible for any model which does not consider individual differences. No such model could be a perfect predictor of all responses, since not all subjects make the same response to each item. The best such a model could do would be to predict, for every item, that response which was chosen by the majority of the subjects. The highest possible accuracy is the sum of the frequencies of majority responses for each item, divided by the total number of responses. In this experiment a model which always made the best possible prediction would predict correctly only 72% of all the responses. By comparison, CLS-1 correctly predicted 61% of the responses. Table 7.3 shows the accuracy of prediction on each problem.

Determination of the performance of the "most accurate" model requires considerable after-the-fact analysis of the data, since the response frequencies to all 179 items must be known. An alternative model using less *post hoc* analysis is always to predict that response most frequent throughout the entire experiment. A model that "predicted" that the subjects never selected a positive instance would correctly predict 65% of the responses. This falls between the 72% maximum prediction and the 61% obtained using CLS-1 (see Table 7.3).

TABLE 7.3

Agreement of Subjects' Responses in Each Problem Predicted by Simulation and *post hoc* Models: Experiment XIII

Problem	Agreement with simulation (%)	Best possible agreement (%)	Agreement if all items called negative (%)
1	56.5	71.3	65.1
2	46.6	70.4	70.4
3	60.8	70.0	68.5
4	67.0	71.6	63.0
5	63.9	73.5	69.4
6	42.0	69.4	63.6
7	59.0	67.9	60.2
8	68.8	71.6	62.7
9	65.4	76.9	67.0
10	66.7	69.1	63.0
11	70.4	77.6	64.5
12	85.2	85.2	74.7
13	53.9	70.0	64.0
14	68.0	69.8	62.0
15	57.4	66.7	59.0
Average	60.9	72.1	65.1

Both the "most accurate" and the "most frequent" prediction strategies have two defects. They cannot be used until the data has been obtained and at least the relative frequencies of responses determined, and both models are methods of maximizing prediction without regard to possible psychological processes involved. An alternate criterion against which simulation performance may be measured is the performance of a randomly chosen subject. As was pointed out in Chapter 6, this is a statistical version of Turing's test. The responses of one subject are used to predict the responses of the other 26 subjects. Table 7.4 reports the results of 26 possible predictions of this sort.[3] The average percentage of correct predictions is slightly lower than that obtained using the simulation. Ten subjects are more accurate predictors of their fellows' responses than is the simulation and 17 are less accurate. Again, CLS-1 passed Turing's test. As in Experi-

[3] The record of one subject was accidentally not included as a predictor.

TABLE 7.4

COMPARISON OF PREDICTIONS OF SUBJECTS' RESPONSES BY USING
SIMULATION OR ANOTHER SUBJECT AS PREDICTOR: EXPERIMENT XIII

Subject used to predict	Predictions (% correct)	Simulation (% correct for 26 subjects)	Best predictor
1	58.0	61.3	Simulation
2	59.9	61.4	Simulation
3	58.6	61.6	Simulation
4	61.9	61.2	Subject
5	61.4	61.3	Subject
6	60.9	61.3	Simulation
7	60.8	61.4	Simulation
8	60.7	61.4	Simulation
9	60.4	61.3	Simulation
10	58.0	61.4	Simulation
11	53.5	61.5	Simulation
12	54.1	61.5	Simulation
13	60.5	61.5	Simulation
14	54.4	61.6	Simulation
15	61.9	61.2	Subject
16	61.4	61.5	Simulation
17	63.2	61.3	Subject
18	62.7	61.3	Subject
19	63.6	61.2	Subject
20	58.3	61.2	Simulation
21	60.4	61.1	Simulation
22	59.6	61.4	Simulation
23	61.6	60.9	Subject
24	63.5	61.3	Subject
25	57.1	61.4	Simulation
26	61.5	61.4	Subject
Average	59.8	61.3	

ment XII, one could not tell, by examining the pattern of responses, whether they were the response of a man or a machine.

The data indicate that CLS-1 is a model of the "general" response tendencies of our subjects, and that when subjects depart from the response predicted by CLS-1 they do not all depart at the same time. This does not mean that there are no consistent individual differences which are not predicted by the model. People might fall into clusters of individuals using similar strategies, such that within a cluster CLS-1 would tend to make bad predictions for every individual on a given item, but this prediction would be randomly good or bad for individuals in other clusters. Stated more simply but less precisely: "Are there groups of people who are more similar to each other than they are to CLS-1, but not more similar to people outside their own group?"

Suppose that this were not true, that instead deviations from the CLS-1 predicted response occurred randomly and independently for each individual. Then if one person agreed with the simulation in some fraction, p_1, of his responses while another agreed on p_2 of his responses, they would be expected to simultaneously disagree with the predicted response (and hence with each other) on $(1 - p_1) \cdot (1 - p_2)$ of their responses. Hence, the expected number of simultaneous disagreements for any two subjects may be calculated on the assumption that there are no consistent individual differences. In 264 of the 361 possible comparisons of pairs of individuals the number of such disagreements exceeded the number that would be expected by chance ($p \leq .05$, using the chi-square technique). Clearly there were subsets of individuals who displayed similar response patterns that were not predicted by CLS-1.

3. DISCUSSION

As in the study of learning the logical connectives, the results of this experiment indicate that CLS-1 is about as good at predicting an individual's responses as another (randomly chosen) subject is. However, the results showing "clustering" of subjects indicate that if, instead of choosing the "predictor" subject at random, we purposely set out to find one who was much more similar to the predictee subject than CLS-1 was, we could do this. A problem for future research is to find a way to identify a good predictor subject for a given predictee, without using the circular definition of examining individual response patterns.

The fact that CLS-1 scores about 60–65% correct predictions out of a maximum possible of 70% indicates that CLS-1 does about as well as any general model of concept learning could do in simulating our subjects' behavior. The key word here is general. As just indicated, we have shown that a program which took into account individual differences could do better. The implications of clustering are, of course, not just limited to the applications of computer models. Our results could be taken as an indication that, at least on such a complex task, no general theory of human learning is possible. If by "general theory of human learning" one means a theory which can predict the responses of each individual in a given situation, this seems a reasonable position. On the other hand, one could maintain that people are utilizing different information processing strategies, and that these strategies are themselves responses which are subject to more general laws of learning. This is a position which seems reasonable to us.

The fact that we found greater agreement between the model and the older, more mathematically trained subjects suggests that general intellectual habits may be very much involved in the solution of this sort of problem. In posttest interviews almost every subject reported that by the 15th problem they had developed a system for finding the classification rule. The logic students, and to a lesser extent the upperclassmen in the history class, were better able to state this rule. In fact, the way in which some of the logic students stated their rule was practically a description of the CLS program. Bartlett's (1958) analogy between thinking and motor skills is appropriate. The logic and history students seemed to have learned certain symbol manipulation techniques (skills) which they could apply immediately to the problem at hand. The younger, perhaps less talented, underclassmen had to develop these techniques during the experimental session.

The above remarks are based entirely on subjective impressions. Further research is needed to develop the points raised. Even if the speculations are correct, this study could not be used as evidence that studying logic, or any other topic, causes people to develop good rules for inductive problem solving. It could be equally true that people who have already developed consistent rules are attracted to the study of logic.

Section IV

Applications and Discussions

CHAPTER 8

Applications of CLS Programs

1. THE CONTENT ANALYSIS PROBLEM

At the beginning we said that one of the reasons for having an artificial intelligence device was to have it do something. An artificial concept learner ought to develop new concepts. Here we report some initial steps toward having CLS programs do just that.

Since the characteristic means of human communication are speech and writing, their importance as sources of information can hardly be over-emphasized. Some information in a text is directed to the matter at hand, other information may reveal more about the speaker than about what is being spoken. The classic summary of a communication is the answer to, "Who says what to whom, how, and with what effect?" Berelson (1954) has focused attention on the "what" in *content analysis*.

In content analysis the units of a document, its words, sentences, or paragraphs, are rated as falling into different categories, such as violence terms, terms with overt or covert sex references, and the like. The assumption of content analysis is that by studying the relative frequency of use of these types of terms a worthwhile picture of the content of the document may be obtained. This picture may often be quite different from the message the speaker intended to convey, just as a psychiatrist's interpretation of a dream may vary from the manifest, obvious theme of the dream. There is no claim that the picture of the document obtained through a given content analysis is a unique description of the document.

Many uses of content analysis involve searches for contrasts between documents from two different sources. Suppose one is given three documents. The first two are of known authorship; the authorship of the third is in dispute. It may be possible, by analysis of the frequency with which certain types of terms appear in the documents, to identify the third document as most probably coming from the author of the first or second document. In this particular use of content analysis, predictability is the only criterion; any clue will do so long as it works. For instance, if one of two authors has a characteristic word, such as "while" instead of "whilst," this fact may be used as a clue in document identification. In document identification, a content analysis based upon the use of terms with some sort of common meaning is only one of several means of solving the problem.

There are other problems in which simple identification is not the only goal. Rather, one may wish to know what, if any, are the "real differences" between the two sets of documents. Also, a "real difference" may be of interest only if it exists within a particular description space. For instance, in the analysis of Egyptian and Indian statements about United States policy toward Cuba, one would be more interested in the differently expressed shades of political intentions in the documents than in whether or not Egyptians and Indians had stylistically different ways of expressing the same idea. The goal here is discovery of theoretically relevant patterns of differences, rather than assignment of an unknown document to a particular source.

In an informal way, very many people have become experts in content analysis. Lawyers, literary critics, psychologists, and politicians need this talent as part of their stock in trade. We know that they have developed very good concepts of such amorphous things as "the writings of an existential psychoanalyst." But what these concepts are and how they were developed is seldom stated. One argument is that the process is too subjective. We explicitly and emphatically disagree; a classification rule and the method by which it was developed ought to be clearly specified. Many of our present classifying rules are useful but not stated. This we regard as an unfortunate, but temporary, deficit in our knowledge. It should be corrected when we know enough about how to develop concepts. As a step in this direction we propose here a technique for recognizing logical patterns in written texts. This technique is explicit in the strongest sense possible; we have constructed it as a string of computer programs, in which CLS's are one of the links.

Before describing the system and results, a strong *caveat* is in order. The studies we report are intended to illustrate a method, not to serve as a report about substantive results in social psychology. To avoid getting into important but detailed side issues, we have not considered here the possibility of reaching the same conclusions with different analytical techniques. In particular, we do not discuss the possibility of using various statistical techniques. Instead, we have reported only the results of using, in the text analysis problem, the CLS programs which have been described in the artificial intelligence studies. This permits the reader to compare the theoretical results from "made-up" problems to the utility of the method in an actual problem.

If one were interested in text analysis, or in any of a variety of statistically similar problems, we would not advocate the blind use of any of the artificial intelligence systems discussed so far. This is because of an essential difference between the problems we use in artificial intelligence studies and those which arise in actual scientific work. In the artificial intelligence studies we can guarantee, because it is part of the rules by which data are collected, that all our descriptions are completely reliable and that the concept to be learned is not probabilistic. As soon as we apply our analysis to "real life" problems, these conditions no longer hold. We will often want to consider probabilistic rules. In this case, the artificial intelligence systems as we have described them must be modified to accept probabilistic discriminations (e.g., stopping at endpoints which classify 90% of the cases reaching them, or stopping when less than 2% of the data remains to be discriminated). At present one of us (P.J.S.) is actively pursuing the application of the CLS programs, including variants which we have not discussed, to the solution of text analysis problems. Some of these techniques involve a combination of concept development and statistical analysis. Others provide for a change in the method of tree development within a single problem. The goal of this work is to learn something about substantive areas of social psychology and sociology through text analysis. The results will be reported in a monograph on content analysis by the Harvard group.

2. THE GENERAL INQUIRER SYSTEM

Before we can use a CLS program we need a method of describing the basic units of text. This was done by the use of the *General Inquirer*, a computer program developed to compile statistics by examining written text (Stone *et al.*, 1962). For our purposes, the General Inquirer can be thought of as having two independent parts, a *dictionary* and a *tagging program*. The dictionary is a set of word stems, e.g., swim, motiv, God, country, Yale. Within the dictionary, subsets of word stems, called *tags* are specified. Each tag represents a general reference which might be assigned to any word within the appropriate subset. For instance, the words buy, sell, lend, and purchase, might be listed under the tag "economic." A word must be listed under at least one tag,[1] and may be listed under more than one.

The tagging program accepts as its input a dictonary and a set of sentences. Each sentence is examined for the occurrence of dictionary word stems in it, and any collection of letters not recognized as a word stem or

[1] Certain words appear in the dictionary without a tag. These are the "filler" words of the English language, such as "the," "and," and "an." Since all these words are treated in an identical manner (they are dropped from further analysis), being in the dictionary without a tag is logically the same as having a special tag. The only practical difference is that further retrievals and analyses cannot be based upon the presence or absence of such words.

word ending is printed out on a "leftover" list. If the text has been pre-
edited by a simple coding scheme (described by Stone *et al.*, 1962), the
syntactical location of each tag in a sentence will also be marked. This
permits the program to recognize differences between such sentences as,
"Teddy Roosevelt dined on bear steaks," and, "Teddy Bear dined on
Roosevelt steaks." We used a very simple syntax coding which recognizes
five categories of words: subjects, objects, verbs, qualifiers, and unclassified.
The necessary pre-editing can be done quickly and accurately by a bright
high-school graduate with a small amount of special training.

An additional feature of the General Inquirer is the insertion of definitions, in dictionary terms, for words not in the dictionary. This is done by
adding a definition in parentheses; the definition then replaces the defined
term in so far as the tagging program is concerned. This is particularly
useful when dealing with slang terms and proper names, which might have
meanings that vary from text to text. The sentence, "Washington never
saw Washington," has a meaning for the General Inquirer if we rewrite
it as, "Washington (military political person) never saw Washington
(city)."

The tagging program produces a magnetic tape containing the sentences
and their associated tags. It also produces a list of statistics about the text
it has tagged; these reflect the frequency of use of each tag in each syntax
position. Both the statistics and the "unrecognized word stem" list are
often useful in guiding a content analysis of the text. The person examining
the text may find in them many leads which can be followed up by examination of specific parts of the original document (Stone and Hunt, 1963).
Information retrieval programs for locating these interesting parts have
been included in the General Inquirer system, but will not be further discussed here.

The tagging program fulfills the role of an industrious but unimaginative
clerk. The investigator, by specifying a dictionary, instructs the tagging
program to make a word count, by sentence and by syntactical location
in the sentence, of a particular document. The tagging program does this
with perfect accuracy, resulting in a concise, readable report.

The next step in a General Inquirer analysis is to select particular tags
as indicating interesting differences between documents. This is normally
the role of the investigator, and how he goes about it will depend upon the
purpose of the analysis. If he is working in what could be called, loosely,
an "inductive" mode, he may concentrate on finding some tag or tags which,
in some combination, appear typical of one document and not of the other
in a contrast. Similarly, if he were looking at only one document, he might
be interested in just finding whatever distribution of tag frequencies might
exist in that document. In other words, he is searching for any tags which

fill some criterion for describing the text with which he is working. An alternate procedure is for the investigator to work in the "hypothesis testing" mode. In this case he will have decided in advance that a particular pattern of tags will be interesting if it actually exists in the data. To take an example, he might state, in advance, that he was interested in knowing whether the writings of Goethe, in his youth and old age, differed in the number of references to engineering. Now it might very well be that there were other ways in which these two sets of writing differed, and some of these other ways might be better statistical discriminators of Goethe's early and late writings. However, in the case of hypothesis testing, this would not be the point. A test would be made just to see if the alleged difference in engineering references did actually exist.

In actual situations, of course, an investigator shuffles back and forth between these two types of investigation. We used CLS programs to help him do this. Among the programs we used are CLS-1, CLS-7, and CLS-8. The latter two have proved useful in further work, and have been expanded to accept probabilistic rules, including various measures of statistical association between tags and sources. Only results using the unmodified programs will be reported here, so that the results can be compared directly to those of the artificial intelligence studies.

Before the CLS programs could be applied, each sentence had to be redescribed as an object with a description stated in terms of attributes and values. This was accomplished by a special translation program which read the syntax-marked sentences as output by the General Inquirer, and described them by the set of ordered pairs (tag, syntax position in which tag is used).

This is a special case of the attribute-value description scheme used by all CLS programs.[2] To illustrate the sort of translation involved, consider the sentence,

Teddy Roosevelt ate a bear.

Pre-edited for syntax position, this sentence may be written as follows:

Teddy Roosevelt (politician)/1 ate/3 a bear/5.

[2] Although any number of tags might appear as attributes in the description of a sentence, a given tag could appear only once. This restriction is necessary in an attribute-value scheme, but is not a requirement in the General Inquirer system. If the General Inquirer assigned a tag in two or more syntactical categories, the position of the tag (i.e., the value of the attribute represented by that tag) was assigned according to the order of priority: subject, object, verb, modifier, and unclassified. This provided five explicit values for each attribute. A sixth value, tag absent, is implicit. More recent systems, developed by Stone and Marshall Smith, do not make this reduction. Instead there is an explicit record of the presence or absence of each combination of tag and syntax.

The numbers following the slashes indicate particular syntax locations. The translation program writes the sentences as a set of ordered pairs: [(political, subject), (person, subject), (consume, verb), (animal, object)].

The General Inquirer dictionary we used contained about 100 tags. Each tag could have one of five possible values (including absence). To get an idea of the potential complexity of the problem one can think of this as a concept learning experiment similar to those described in the chapters on simulation, but with nonsense syllables 100-characters long, each character position having five different possible letters.

To illustrate how the CLS program worked in content analysis, we offer the following flip, but we hope illustrative, example. Imagine an analysis of letters written home by two students, A. Bookworm and R. A. Rah. Bookworm begins by talking either of things he did to academic subjects or things that young ladies did to him. Rah, on the other hand, talks about what academic subjects did to him or about what he did to young ladies. Figure 8.1 shows two decision trees which might be used to discriminate sentences written by Bookworm from those written by Rah. Notice that the concept can be represented by two tree forms, and either one will do equally well. In general we shall find that in text analysis several trees may be written to discriminate between any given pair of documents. Mathematically, this is an indication that the data do not contain sufficient information to define uniquely a single discrimination rule. Psychologically, this reduces to the statement that most documents differ in more than one way.

This example oversimplifies text analysis in an important way, since it is assumed that neither source (Rah nor Bookworm) ever generates sentences with exactly the same description. In point of fact, there are so many different ways for sentences to differ that we seldom find two sentences in different documents with exactly the same representation. When this event does occur, the program recognizes it. More common, and more difficult to handle, is the case in which a contrast is made between two documents and then verified on a second pair of documents. In the first pair some sentence may occur only in text from one source which may, for no particularly interesting reason, be just as likely to occur in documents from the other source at a later time. To return to our previous example, suppose that the students do share two common topics of conversation, a desire for money and for clean laundry. Tactfully, they do not bring up these points in every letter home. The following samples of text are collected:

From Bookworm

I received *A* in all my courses. I have amazed my history teacher with my brilliance. The blonde in my English class stares at me every day. She flatters me before exam-

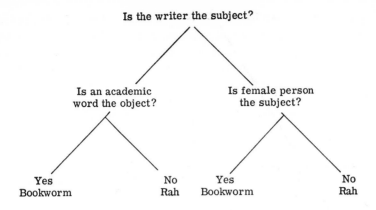

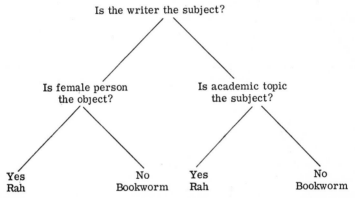

Fig. 8.1. Possible decision trees for distinguishing between writings of two hypothetical students.

inations. She used to avoid me earlier in the semester. I need some money to buy a new slide rule.

Lovingly,
Al

From Rah

Yesterday I took Marjorie for a ride in the park. I dated Alice for the prom. Your boy really dazzled Joan Wednesday! By the way, my history teacher called me an ignoramus. Dr. Moosmilk flunked me in history. Have you sent the 10 tuxedo shirts yet?

Affectionately,
Rob

The decision tree shown in Fig. 8.2 will identify any given sentence as being from one of these two documents. It fails, however, to give an accu-

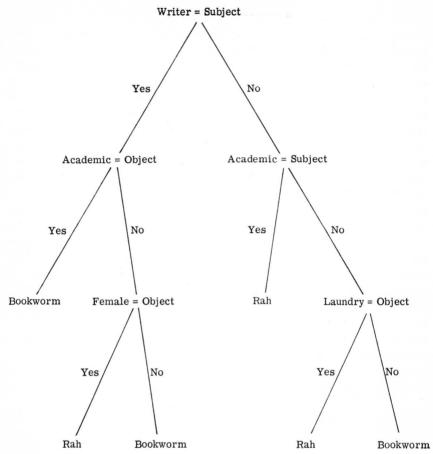

Fig. 8.2. Tree for discriminating Rah from Bookworm based on first pair of letters home in second example.

rate identification of the source of every sentence in the following two new letters:

From Bookworm

I am not doing as well in class. I underwhelmed my math professor. The brunette in biology lab winked at me. Please send a tie.

> Lovingly yours,
> Al

From Rah

The Dean took me off probation. Biology no longer terrifies me. I did not try to date the redhead again. Please send an advance on next month's allowance.

> Affectionately,
> Rob

The endpoints on the far right of the tree of Fig. 8.2 do not give the correct classification of the last sentence in either note. This illustrates the first point: a given sample of documents will usually contain some sentences which were emitted by one source on a fortuitous basis. On the next sample the same sentences may be emitted by the other source. There is no way to know in advance whether sentences that are apparently unique to a source are truly characteristic of that source or reflect some temporary effect specific to the topic about which the source is writing. In fact, topic will usually be the major determinant of content, since most authors adjust their writings to reflect what they are writing about. Logically this poses no problem, since the program will accept as coming from a given source any document which is so marked. This is one of the reasons why detailed text analysis studies using CLS programs ought to use programs which accept some sort of probabilistic decision making rule.

In the following examples a text analysis system was created by combining the General Inquirer with a CLS program and a particular dictionary, known as the second General Inquirer dictionary.[3] This dictionary, which establishes the basic description space within which the CLS program must operate, was designed for use in social psychology. It has since been superseded by a more carefully developed dictionary for this field, and by various specialized dictionaries for text analysis in anthropology, survey research, and political science.

3. CALIFORNIA MONEY BILLS: AN EXAMPLE FROM POLITICS

Our first example is a relatively simple one, chosen because it is small enough to be discussed conveniently and because it does not require specialized knowledge of subject matter. Also, and perhaps more important at this stage, we have a general idea of the sort of answer which the system should develop.

California is notorious for requiring its citizens to act as legislators. Money bills and legal regulations which, in most states, would be considered the business of the legislature often require direct approval of the electorate.

[3] The original system was written using the General Inquirer COMIT program (Yngve, 1961), a COMIT program to translate General Inquirer output to the format required for input to the IPL-V program representing CLS, and the IPL-V programs for the various CLS versions used. The latter programs were modified to allow for storage of data on auxiliary tapes, but otherwise they were unchanged from those used in the artificial intelligence studies. The pilot system, from which most of our examples are taken, was debugged and used to prove the feasibility of the method at the Western Data Processing Center, UCLA, in 1962. The systems now in use are both more compact and faster. Systems have been programmed for the IBM 7094, the IBM 1401 (in which the steps at each node are chosen by hand), and the MIT Project MAC time sharing system.

As a result, the typical California ballot will present the voter with 20 to 30 reasonably complex issues. To aid him in decision making, the Secretary of State distributes a booklet describing the various propositions on the ballot. This booklet contains brief arguments by proponents and opponents of each measure. In 1962 an unusual event occurred: substantially the same proposal appeared on the ballot twice. Proposition 1, a proposal arising in the State Assembly, would have authorized an increase in the pay of state legislators to $11,000 a year. Proposition 17, a proposal by the State Senate, would have raised salaries to $10,500. Owing to legal requirements, separate paragraphs were included in the booklet urging and opposing each measure. As might be expected, the arguments appear to the casual reader to be logically identical in each case. (The voters evidently perceived them as such and responded in a consistent manner; both proposals were defeated.)

Twenty-five sentences were selected from the arguments for and against Proposition 1 and 28 sentences from those for and against Proposition 17. Sentences which obviously indicated the source, such as those containing the phrase "Vote no . . .", were excluded. Compound sentences were reworded as two simple sentences.

The arguments of Proposition 1 were contrasted using the text analysis system consisting of a General Inquirer program plus an analysis by CLS-1. The resulting concept is shown in Fig. 8.3. This decision rule breaks down the 24 original sentences into six subtypes, one subtype corresponding

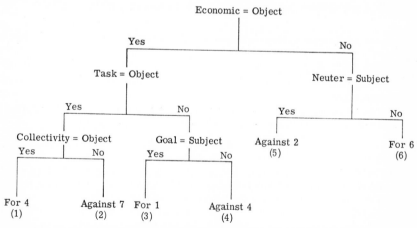

FIG. 8.3. Concept tree developed using Proposition 1 as first step in a series of analysis. Endpoint numbers are shown in parentheses for reference to text.

to each endpoint of the tree. The sentences at each endpoint are as follows (key text words are italicized; some text words cause more than one tag).

Endpoint (1), for issue: economic as object, task as object, collectivity as object.
  Four sentences:

Taxpayers have not increased *legislative salaries* since 1954.

Men and women with the knowledge, education, and experience required to make them valuable members of the legislature are able to draw (receive) far higher *salaries* in private *industry*.

Expecting them (legislators) also to earn a living at their own *business* or *profession* is unreasonable.

Legislative salaries are far below those (*salaries*) paid in the co-equal *judicial* and *executive* branches of state *government*.

Endpoint (2), against issue: economic as object, task as object, collectivity *not* as object.
  Seven sentences:

Although the overwhelming majority of voters repeatedly rejected *pay* increases for members of legislatures at prior elections.

They here seek *pay* increases for members of legislature by subterfuge.

This proposal does not even mention the amount of the *pay* increase.

Which (*pay* increase) would be authorized by the proposed constitutional amendment.

This measure limits the *pay* of an assemblyman or senator to one-half (fraction) that (pay) received by a United States Congressman.

Again and again the legislature over protests has adopted new *tax spending programs*.

We (writers) feel that any approval of a salary increase legislators would take (interpret) as voter approval of this *spending program*.

Endpoint (3), for issue: economic as object, task *not* as object, goal as subject.
  One sentence:

The *privilege* of service should not entail *financial* penalty.

Endpoint (4), against issue: economic as object, task *not* as object, goal *not* as subject.
  Four sentences:

The legislature already has *benefited*.

For every *dollar* legislators contribute to their own retirement.

Taxpayers now contribute four *dollars*.

(Legislature) building up a grave threat to the *taxpayers* of 1964, 1965, 1966, and the succeeding years immediately ahead of us.

Endpoint (5), against issue: economic *not* as object, neuter role as subject.
  Two sentences:

Cleverly, (they) worded this measure.

Members (legislators) with long service can even retire at full pay.

Endpoint (6), for issue: economic *not* as object, neuter role *not* as subject.
  Six sentences:

The tasks of legislators have grown in volume and complexity in recent years.
While the satisfaction of public service well performed is rewarding.
It (satisfaction) will not pay the family bills.

And (expectation) forces an unnecessary personal burden on the members (legislators).

The legislative salaries will be less than half the average salaries of judges and department heads. [*Note:* The appearance of an economic term in the subject negates the appearance of the term in the object (cf. footnote 2). In more recent procedures it would be placed correctly at terminal one.]

Compensatory adjustment is generally acknowledged to be long overdue to the membership of the California legislature.

On examination of these trees, several features become apparent. We shall mention two. First, the tree primarily centers on the positive information of the sentences against the issue. Half the sentences for the issue are sent to the endpoint at the far right, an endpoint which is completely defined in terms of negative information. While the sentences at this endpoint do not refer to "economic" as an object or "neuter role" as a subject, they form a very heterogeneous class as to what they do say. Secondly, several of the tags used in the tree are of very minor importance. "Goal" as a subject is used to separate but one "pro" sentence from a group of four "con" sentences; it is doubtful whether this node would be very useful in further trees. "Neuter" as a subject functions with only slightly more importance.

A second way to summarize trees is to do the summary automatically by repeated application of the CLS program to new data. The method begins by comparing two documents, one from each source. Call this contrast 0. At contrast 1 two new documents from the same source are examined. The system attempts to classify all the sentences in the new documents using the decision tree developed at contrast 0. Those sentences which are incorrectly classified are disregarded. The remaining sentences are assumed to be more typical of their sources, since they are sentences which can be classified by rules developed from independent data. The assumption is, of course, not always correct. If the original rules were developed from aberrant data (i.e., if the first and second contrasts do not really represent replications), some typical sentences will be thrown out of the second analysis. If the first decision tree is a random classifier of non-typical sentences, some of these will be included in the second analysis. Still it seems reasonable to expect that in many situations the set of correctly classified sentences at the second contrast will contain a higher proportion of sentences which characterize their sources.

The arguments for and against Proposition 1 were used as contrast 0 and the arguments for and against Proposition 17 as contrast 1. The tree was developed at contrast 0 (Fig. 8.3), and correctly classified 21 of 28 sentences in Proposition 17 arguments. These 21 sentences were used to develop the tree shown in Fig. 8.4. Although this tree was developed on almost as much data as the tree shown in Fig. 8.3, it is much simpler and easier to interpret. Every one of the seven "typical" sentences arguing against an increase in salary contained both quantitative and economic references. The phrase "raise taxes more" comes to mind. The text analysis suggests that examination of those individual sentences containing tag

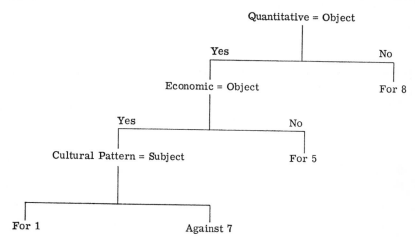

Fɪɢ. 8.4. Contrast arguments on Proposition 17: California Ballot Issues.

terms for quantitative and economic references would reveal what the crucial arguments against the bill were. Again, we would be less confident in stating that we could locate the sentences containing crucial arguments for the bill (although the tree does suggest some interesting leads), since such sentences are generally defined by the absence of tags.

The analysis so far is, in a way, proving the obvious. There are probably quite a few California voters who could have told us that this is what the issue was about without our going to so much trouble. This is especially true when we discuss two arguments about issues which (up to the level of $500 per legislator per year) are really identical. The advantage we have over the California voter is that we can say exactly what steps the General Inquirer CLS-1 system went through to arrive at its conclusions.

Another more searching question is whether the leads developed from this analysis can be useful in studying other issues which, though not exactly the same, do have some common facets. From the above analysis alone we would not be willing to say that all Californian political arguments revolve around economics. The analysis does suggest that many of the key sentences in arguments about money bills do contain economic terms, surely not an unreasonable conclusion. If it is true, we should be able to make a reasonably accurate summary of such a political issue by locating sentences containing quantitative and economic references.

4. SUICIDE NOTES: A PSYCHIATRIC EXAMPLE

Our second example is one in which the content analysis system does not work particularly well. This may be because the "source" we considered is really composed of separate sources, each with its own characteristic style of writing.

Shneidman and Farberow (1957) collected notes left by 32 actual suicide cases. For each individual note writer they found a presumably nonsuicidal individual (an effort was made to ensure that this was true) who was matched with the note writer on a variety of socio-economic variables such as age, sex, religion, and occupation. The nonsuicidal individual was then asked to write a "simulated" suicide note. Shneidman and Farberow published both the actual and simulated notes.

Some 100 sentences were selected from these notes, divided into contrasts averaging 25 sentences per document, and processed by the sequential analysis technique described in the previous section. The CLS-8 program was used. The concept developed at the initial contrast was quite large; in fact, it could not be reproduced legibly on a standard-size page. The tree developed at the second stage (Figure 8.5) was much more compact. As it

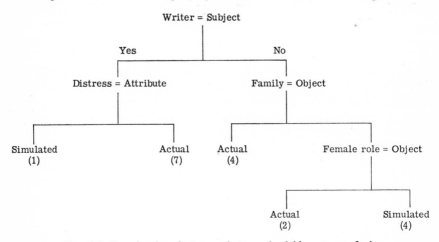

Fig. 8.5. Tree developed at second stage of suicide notes analysis.

stands, this decision tree does suggest some interesting retrievals. Note particularly that sentences with the writer as the subject and distress terms as qualifiers appear to be more characteristic of the simulated than of the actual suicide notes. This may be somewhat counterintuitive, however, for the very reason that this is what the persons simulating suicide notes think they should say. Also, the actual suicides appear, in this analysis, to make more references to family and female terms than do the suicide simulators.

These differences are interesting because they are similar to some of the discriminations found using a non-CLS procedure applied to considerably more data. Using comparisons on matched pairs, Ogilvie *et al.* (1962) were able to predict correctly the source of a message in 17 out of 18 comparisons. Unfortunately, our CLS was not set up to handle paired document contrasts, so the analogous contrasts were not made.

5. FUTURE BIOGRAPHIES: AN EXAMPLE FROM SOCIAL ANTHROPOLOGY

The following example, taken from work in sociology and anthropology, demonstrates an interplay in which automated content analysis is used as a guide in selecting statistical tests.

Gillespie and Allport (1955) asked students to write their "autobiographies as of the year 2000" in an attempt to get some idea of how they felt the world would develop. We focused our attention on passages written by Egyptian women students and by coeds at Radcliffe College, Harvard University. As might be expected, casual reading indicates that these people had quite different views of the future.

Four passages of 90–100 sentences, two each from a Radcliffe and an Egyptian student, were selected for analysis. Two "Radcliffe-Egypt" pairs were selected as contrasts 0 and 1 in a sequential analysis using CLS-8. In addition, the second contrast was analyzed independently. The final tree obtained in the sequential analysis and the two independently developed concepts developed using each contrast alone were examined to see (a) if they revealed consistently discovered branches, and (b) if any of the divisions above an endpoint, although not sufficient to divide the sentences below that node into Radcliffe or Egypt sentences exclusively, were statistically significant discriminators.

The concepts developed by contrasting the two pairs of documents directly were cumbersome (both contained more than 30 test nodes), but did display certain regularities. Of particular interest are the tests at the root and at nodes close to it, since these tests are developed from a larger body of data than are the lower-order nodes.

In both contrasts the test at the root was, "Is the author the subject of the sentence?" Both Radcliffe and Egyptian students have themselves as the subjects of about half their sentences. They differ in what they say next. Consider the nodes to the lower left of the root, i.e., the question next asked of all sentences for which the answer to the first was "yes." In both contrasts the question was, "Is there a time reference in the verb?" and appeared within two nodes to the lower left of the root. The sequential analysis tree had the "time" question immediately to the lower left of the root.

Figure 8.6 shows the relevant portion of the sequential analysis concept, with the number of Egyptian and Radcliffe sentences routed to each branch (these are not endpoints) below the second node. As indicated in the figure, the split between Radcliffe and Egyptian sentences is statistically significant at the .05 level. Since this particular tree is the product of the second of the contrasts, the precise form of the following rule is simply

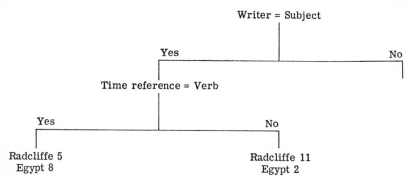

Fig. 8.6. Left-hand branch of sequential analysis tree: second stage of Radcliffe-Egypt analysis.

too complex to use: "*If* a sentence is correctly classified by the concept developed at the first contrast, and *if* it contains an author reference as the subject, and *if* a time reference is in the verb, *then* the writer is probably an Egyptian. If the sentence fulfills the first two criteria but does not have a time reference in the verb, then the author is probably a Radcliffe student." It does suggest that a further analysis be made of the use of personal and time references in this data.

In the independent analysis of the second contrast (i.e., an analysis of all sentences in the second pair of documents, not just those correctly classified by the first concept developed), the combination of root and second question produced a significant dichotomy. The relevant portion of the decision tree is shown in Fig. 8.7. Thirty-two of the Radcliffe students' sentences had the author as subject, but only two of these had "ought" (imperative) terms in the verb. The Egyptian student, on the other hand, had nearly as many sentences with herself as the subject (29) and almost half of them contained "ought" terms in the verb. The difference is significant at better than the .01 level.

So far we have dealt only with sentences which the authors wrote about themselves. In the independent analysis of both contrasts the node to the lower right of the root, i.e., the node containing the first question asked about sentences for which the author was *not* the subject, specified the same question, "Is a family term present in the verb?" Family terms in verbs refer to actions which normally take place in a familial context. Figure

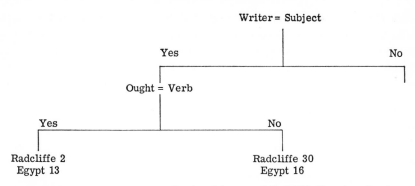

Fɪɢ. 8.7. Part of concept tree developed in second Radcliffe-Egypt contrast.

8.8 shows the relevant portion of the tree, and summarizes the accuracy of this question in discriminating Radcliffe and Egyptian sentences. As before, the question is a conditional one: "Given that the author is not the subject, is there a family term in the verb?" In the first contrast the question did significantly discriminate between Radcliffe and Egyptian sentences; in the second contrast the differences were not significant but were in the expected direction. If the two contrasts are regarded as independent samples, we may partition chi-square to determine (a) whether or not the average discriminating power of the question is significant, and (b) whether or not there is a difference between the two contrasts. (The technique is discussed briefly by Snedecor, 1956, p. 214, and in more detail by Sutcliffe, 1957.) The over-all discriminating power of the question is confirmed by this analysis, and no difference between groups is indicated. We would

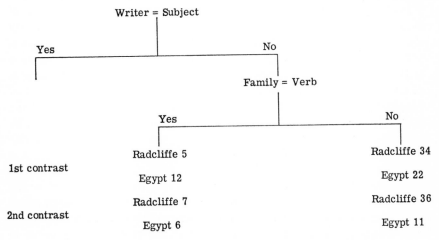

Fɪɢ. 8.8. Use of family reference in verb: Radcliffe-Egypt analysis.

be particularly confident of this discriminator because it has been confirmed in a replication with independent data. Notice that for source identification it would have to be used on a relative basis. Given two documents, one guaranteed to be from each source, it would make sense to assign the document with the greater fraction of "author not subject, family term in verb" sentences to the Egyptian source. However, we would not expect that a great many such sentences would be found in either source. Again, we would not recommend that this rule be used for source identification. Rather, we would like to see a more extensive investigation of just how family references are used in these texts.

6. SOME ANTICIPATED DEVELOPMENTS IN AUTOMATIC CONTENT ANALYSIS

To date, the principal use of automatic theme analysis has been to suggest leads, to indicate particular parts of a text which are worth further examination. In scanning documents by computer, the CLS program plays a role analogous to the role played by automated decision-making procedures in the air defense task. In air defense a large number of aircraft sightings are input to a screening system. A computerized decision process recognizes most of these sightings as routine and passes them on. A few signals will be retained for a more searching, second-level analysis, and a few of these passed to a third level, and so on. Eventually it may be necessary to "scramble" an interceptor aircraft to examine one of the incoming flights visually. The final decision to attack is always made by a person. The system works because the human being plus the computer can handle far more data than the human being working alone.[4]

Content analysis involves much the same steps. The tag tallies produced by the General Inquirer and the trees produced by different CLS programs represent summaries of different types and complexity. Whether or not CLS programs provide good summaries is a question which cannot be answered without a good deal of practical experience. Practical experience in other fields completely outside of content analysis will also be necessary before the CLS methods of developing sequential decision rules can be evaluated fully. Some work on different problems is currently under way.

The experience we have obtained so far with the content analysis application has indicated some problems which will probably always appear. These revolve around the choice of an appropriate heuristic for establishing test nodes. The problem of accepting probabilistic discriminators has already been discussed; to discuss all the other problems would require a separate treatise on induction and optimum decision making.

[4] A further, unclassified discussion is given by Green (1963).

There is one problem, however, that does keep recurring. This is the problem of uncovering interactions. Suppose one has two attributes, A and B, which, taken together, can be used to identify the source of 80% of the data but which, when taken alone can be used to identify the source of less than 40% of the data. If there is a third variable, C, which is more accurate than A or B taken alone, but less accurate than the two taken together, it is hard to see how any system which tests for the accuracy of single attributes at a given point (node) can avoid choosing the third variable. The problem of interactions of this and other sorts has arisen several times in theme analysis. It is particularly vexing when a very large number of attributes are to be investigated (as is typically the case in text analysis), since it becomes impractical to test all possible combinations of n attributes taken together. It seems doubtful that a single heuristic tree-developing procedure can be found which will satisfy all the criteria for uncovering interactions that one might specify. Further studies, both by mathematical analysis of "tree development"and by additional artificial intelligence experiments, will probably be required to determine how particular CLS techniques will perform in different situations.

A quite different approach to the practical development of decision trees has been constructed as an aid in the solution of specific problems of text analysis. The idea behind this variation is that no general routine for defining subproblems is likely to be appropriate in all phases of a text analysis problem. In fact, one should be free to alter his heuristics as the problem develops. While such a proposal makes the mathematical analysis of CLS's exceedingly difficult, if not impossible, it does have practical attraction for those interested in solving specific concept learning problems for their own sake.

The Harvard text analysis project (under the direction of PJS) has constructed a man-machine program which operates as a CLS with a human controller.[5] The controller designates a definite CLS subproblem-definition heuristic to be used at each node. His choices include, but are not limited to, the programs we have discussed; such rules as, "Choose a sufficient but not necessary rule, such that some items of type A and no items of type not A have the chosen characteristic," are included. The controller may also influence the system according to his particular theoretical interests, such as directing the program to ignore x exceptions to an otherwise satisfactory rule. The program applies the rule selected, and indicates the shape of the partially grown tree by printing out the relevant information. The controller responds by indicating how subproblems are to be defined at the next node to be attacked, the computer acts, and the process is repeated

[5] This technique should prove particularly useful as time sharing computer systems are developed, as such systems make man-machine interaction far more feasible.

until the final tree is developed. At any time the controller may terminate the process. He may do this if he decides that beyond his current node the variation between sources represents random fluctuations, or for some other reason.

In an unpublished paper Daniel Ogilvie, of the Harvard group, applied this method of text analysis to the problem of understanding the difference between the reactions of two Harvard students to a "psychiatrically oriented" discussion in which they had both participated. By using the computer's ability to reorder the data rapidly, Ogilvie was able to look at the appearance of many different attributes in the students' speech, in many different contexts. For example, he could ask for almost immediate counts of such complex sentences as "sentences which reach the seventh node on the right and contain aggression references." The processes by which Ogilvie analyzed the data were essentially those which a clinical psychologist might go through in analyzing a case—he looked at different sentences in the context in which they occurred, progressively redividing the data until he obtained what he thought was a sensible picture of the personality of the students whom he was examining. Ogilvie reports that he felt he had learned something about them which he might not otherwise have learned. At the same time he points out that the procedure has certain pitfalls. Trees developed by the man-machine interaction are recorded accurately enough, and this facility to recreate the step-by-step processes of the "artist's approach" to text analysis is itself worthwhile. However, the relative excellence of the decision rule obtained is unknown. Because the reason for choosing particular subproblem definitions at particular points varies, and is often hard to state, there seems to be no hope of finding the extent to which the resulting concept capitalizes on chance fluctuations in the basic data. The only way to make sure that the rule as such holds up is to test it on new data.

7. APPLICATION TO MEDICAL STATISTICS

The CLS procedure has also been applied to quite a different field, medical data analysis. In medicine fairly large files of records may be obtained in the course of routine hospital administration or from a special survey. Such records are often examined in order to plan an intensive, and perhaps expensive, specialized investigation. A drawback to this research strategy is that it is difficult to organize large files of records to reveal complex interactions in a manner that can be understood by the human investigator. Some help can be obtained by using computer oriented techniques of information retrieval, such as a program to print selected two- and three-way tables plotting one variable against another. The investigator still must nominate the variables in which he is interested, since such programs have no way of discovering "interesting" patterns on their own. A CLS program, on the other hand, is designed to do precisely this.

To obtain some added field experience with the CLS technique, a version of CLS-9 was programmed for the University of Sydney's English Electric KDF-9 computer, and members of the School of Medicine of the University of Sydney were invited to submit data for analysis. In this section we report some of the results which were obtained. As in the case of the content analysis studies, we stress that this is done to illustrate a method and not to report substantive findings in medicine. The medical significance of the analysis is properly the concern of the original investigators, and will be reported as they think fit and through normal publication channels.[6]

CLS-9 was chosen because it can be shown, on logical grounds alone, to provide the most accurate "partial" tree for a given body of data. This point is covered in Chapter 5, Section 7, and in more detail in a separate technical article (Hunt, 1964b). The reader may recall that in Chapter 5, Section 7 it was shown that CLS-9 did not perform particularly well if it was required to readjust its decision rules in the face of new data, i.e., that it did not perform well in a limited memory situation. Since in the medical analysis case all the data could be made available for analysis at the beginning of the run, problems associated with limited memory do not arise.

The CLS-9 program used was changed trivially from the one described in Chapter 5, Section 7. To improve running speed and, more crucially, to economize on the amount of internal computer memory used, the program was recoded in USER CODE, the KDF-9's machine-oriented assembly language. A special routine was included to handle the case in which two objects with the same description are found in two different criterion classes. As was pointed out in discussing text analysis, this is a case that could not occur in the artificial intelligence experiments but obviously does occur in practical applications. Finally, the program was modified to print out ancillary statistics on the distribution of cases into each of the criterion classes at each node. This aids the investigator in determining the statistical reliability of the decision rule at any point in the tree.

Three substantive problems were investigated. The Department of Surgery provided two sets of data which, although different in content, were logically very similar. In one case some 60 variables had been measured on 140 patients who, following surgery, had developed one of four forms of infection in the wound site. The problem was to determine which, if

[6] We wish to thank the members of the School of Medicine, Professor J. Lowenthal and Mr. R. Gye of the Department of Surgery, and Professor C. R. B. Blackburn and Dr. W. Arter of the Department of Medicine for making their data available for this analysis.

any, combinations of the 60 variables could be used to predict the type of infection found in each patient. In the second study, 50 variables were measured on 50 patients who had sustained severe head injuries. The problem was to find predictors of the course of recovery. Thus both problems involve the analysis of substantial records from an intermediate number of patients. The sample is not tiny, neither do we have hundreds or thousands of sample points for every variable. Since the two problems are logically so similar, only the wound survey will be discussed.

As in the larger text analysis problems, the complete decision tree from the wound survey data was too large to be represented conveniently in a book. Also, many of the lower order tests were not statistically reliable. The discriminations made at the root node or close to it, being based on large parts of the sample, were of more interest. The initial question recommended by CLS-9 was, "How long did the wound drain following surgery?" For wounds draining 24 hours or less only a nonspecific type of infection was found. (There was no control group consisting of persons without post-surgical infection.) For persons whose wounds had drained for less than 24 hours, the program recommended a further question, "What ward was the patient in?" For these patients there was an interaction between type of wound infection and ward, for patients with heavier drainage there was no such interaction. This makes sense if one thinks of wound infection by a particular microorganism as a chance event depending upon the coincidence of the microorganism and an open wound. The probability of infection of a wound will depend jointly upon the length of time the wound is open and the density of the microorganisms around the patient. If the wound is open for a long time, infection is a virtual certainty and the effect of density will not be apparent. A CLS program can detect such interactions.

The Department of Medicine presented us with a problem of a different type, one in which there were only a few measurements on each member of a large sample. The particular research project was a study of the epidemiology of liver disease in Australian (Eastern) New Guinea. In this area, which is one of the most primitive in the world, liver disease is widespread. In an attempt to determine some of the factors associated with abnormal livers, a survey was conducted, in which some 1800 natives were examined. The sample was drawn from two districts, the Eastern and Western Highlands, which are about 150 miles apart. Each person in the sample was examined rapidly to determine a few salient facts about his personal history, current physical condition, and whether or not he had any indication of malfunctioning liver. The data was analyzed by the CLS-9 program in three passes, one in which a decision rule was formed for all available data, and in separate passes for the eastern and western districts. This was done to parallel other analyses in which the two districts were compared, because it was suspected that the pattern of liver disease might vary in different geographic areas.

As we have typically found, the complete decision trees were large and unwieldy. However, if one traces the tree up to the point at which statistical reliability is lost, apparently meaningful patterns appear. The diagnostic categories used were related to liver enlargement: none, less than, and greater than 4 cm. Over the entire sample (and in both districts) roughly two out of every three people showed no evidence of liver enlargement. For those persons who displayed mild edema (swelling of tissues) this ratio was almost reversed, as the CLS-9 analysis showed. However, edema was itself an unusual condition. For people without edema, the best predictor of liver enlargement was spleen enlargement, another fact revealed by the questions selected by the program. Furthermore, in the western district only, and considering only persons without edema or spleen enlargement, the program selected sex as a predictor of liver enlargement. The incidence of abnormal liver condition was higher in women than men. Note that we are not saying that this was not true in both districts. The statement is that only in the western district was the statement both true *and* a better predictor of size of liver than any other piece of information gathered. Again considering only those people in the western district without spleen enlargement or edema, the program reported that for men no single variable could be found which would aid in prediction of liver enlargement more than guessing the most likely alternative (no enlargement), but that for women liver enlargement was correlated with age. Examination of the appropriate frequencies did reveal a correlation. Only 45 of the 201 otherwise normal women under 30 had enlarged livers, while 50 of the 91 women over 30 who were examined were found to have enlarged livers. For men, on the other hand, only 50 of some 350 normal subjects showed liver enlargement, and in no age group did the incidence of enlarged livers exceed 50%. As with any *post hoc* analysis, it is advisable to check these interactions against new data. This will be done in a larger survey. Some of the decision rules suggested in the analysis of medical data had been suspected by the investigators who, after all, would and should have acquired a good intuitive picture of their data as they collected it. The program was of help in organizing their data for them rather than as a *deus ex machina* which found completely unsuspected patterns. This is as it should be, and we would certainly not advocate blind obedience to CLS derived decision rules when they are contradicted by the investigator's intuition. (We repeat our warning: the examples in this section are intended to illustrate a method, not to report medical facts.) What we do feel is that in the case of conflict between CLS decision rules and conclusions drawn from other procedures, the assumptions made by both the CLS program and the other procedures be examined carefully so that the cause of the conflict can be understood. This, of course, is the sensible use of any statistical technique.

CHAPTER 9

The CLS in the Context of Other Research

1. THE GENERAL PATTERN RECOGNITION PROBLEM

We have applied the name "concept learning" to a particular type of pattern recognition problem. Because of its theoretical interest and because of the many practical applications a pattern recognizer would have, the general problem has attracted a good deal of attention in the recent literature. In addition, several limited schemes for solving particular classes of pattern recognition problems have been proposed. How do CLS programs fit into the attempts to develop an automatic pattern recognizer?

A mathematical formulation of the general problem has been given by Sebesteyen (1962), who has shown that within this formulation the optimal pattern recognition system can be defined, under various criteria for optimality. He goes on to show that while, in many cases, the actual realization of such a classification rule would not be practical, there are useful approximate techniques. Since the CLS represents an approximation technique somewhat different from those he considers, but still fits within his general framework, his work serves as a good point at which to begin the discussion.

We have indicated that stating an object's description is equivalent to locating the object in an n-dimensional space, but cautioned against defining "closeness" in this space, since the values of attributes were not ordered. Suppose, for a moment, that it is sensible to regard the values as ordered, i.e., that an object with value 2 of attribute 1 is, insofar as attribute 1 is concerned, more like an object with a value of 1 than is a third object with a value of 3. In fact, let us go further and assume that the space is continuous, so that the assigning of particular values represents an arbitrary amount of approximation. For simplicity of representation, think also of a space of two dimensions. The remarks to be made generalize readily to the n-dimensional case.

Consider a case in which every object within the universe is to be divided into one of two classes. Each object corresponds to a point in the description space. The classes are said to be linearly separable if a line (hyperplane in a higher order space) exists such that every point in one class falls on one side of the line, and every point in the other class falls on the other side.

The pattern recognition problem is the problem of determining the line separating the two classes.

To take a concrete example, consider the classification problem presented in Fig. 9.1. The circles and plus signs do not fall neatly into two groups of points defined either by the x or y value of a point. However, line L separates the classes. To determine whether a given point is a plus sign or a

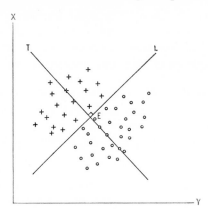

FIG. 9.1. Example of two linearly separable classes.

circle, one should find on which side of L it lies. A way to do this is to construct the line T perpendicular to L. Any point in the original space (i.e., any object) will have a projection on T which may be determined if the original coordinates of the point are known. Knowledge of the appropriate classification follows immediately.

The determination of T is well known (the details are discussed by Sebesteyen). If we consider the distance of any two points to be the distance between their projections on T, one may find a T such that it maximizes the mean square distance between the mean projection of each group on T (i.e., maximizes the mean square distance between groups) while holding the mean square distance between points within a group constant.

In terms of mechanization of the resulting classification rule, a device can easily be envisaged which conducts n tests, one on each of the original dimensions of an object to be classified, and then assigns the object to the appropriate class. If one regards the sample of points used to define T as having been obtained by random sampling of points defined by normally distributed variables, the resulting discriminant is identical to that obtained using the statistical technique of multiple discriminant analysis (Anderson, 1958; Rao, 1952). Thus, if one is willing to assume that the sample of points was drawn from a larger universe in which each point in a class is located randomly along each of the n dimensions, the arguments for classical statistical analysis can be presented to argue that this is the best possible rule for pattern classification.

Determining the discriminant function, T, as a linear combination of the original dimensions is a straightforward mathematical operation which, though tedious, is not beyond the bounds of modern computing machinery, unless the number of dimensions in the space is very large indeed (greater than 400 is a reasonable figure). The limiting point in the computation is inversion of the n-dimensional square matrix of covariance terms representing the correlations between measurements on each of the original dimensions.

Complications to this picture can readily be envisaged. First, suppose that there were more than two classes of objects to be discriminated. This can easily be handled by adding additional discriminant lines, either for class A, B, or C against the rest, or for class A vs. class B, class B vs. C, and class A vs. C. A geometrical example of the procedure is shown in Fig. 9.2. Mathematical techniques for determining each decision point

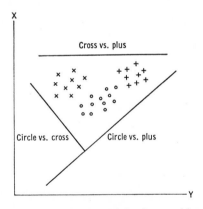

Fig. 9.2. Example of multiple class problem.

exist and are quite straightforward. Again, they are limited only by the necessity of finding the inverse of a square matrix of order n. Another problem that arises is that there will be, for K classes, $\frac{1}{2}K(K-1)$ discriminants. Thus the amount of computation will increase rapidly.

An alternate technique has been presented by Sebesteyen. In this technique K linear functions are computed, one for each class, which *minimize* the mean square distance (projection on the corresponding line) *within* each of the K classes while holding the distance between groups constant. In classification, the probability of finding a point at a given location assuming that it is actually a member of the kth class $k = 1$,

. . . , K) is determined. The point is assigned to the class for which this probability is a maximum. If weights are introduced to represent the cost of various types of misclassification, the second method of determining a classification by linear functions of the original variables may be shown to yield the best solution by a Bayesian criterion—the total cost of misclassification will be minimized. This solution will not, in general, be realized by multiple discriminant functions.

The Bayesian alternative is also limited by the necessity of inverting a matrix of order n.

A more serious complication occurs when the original pattern recognition problem does not meet the criterion for linear separability. An example of this is shown in Fig. 9.3, and we point out that problems I.4 and I.5 (Fig. 2.3) may be represented in this way. No linear function of x and y can be found that will separate the crosses from the circles in Fig. 9.3. However,

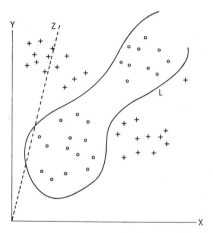

Fig. 9.3. An example of a classification problem that is not linearly separable.

a nonlinear function, L, could be found that would draw a curve around all circles, excluding all plus signs. Sebesteyen illustrates this by analogy to a relief map. We may think of a ridge, whose base was delineated by the line L. The altitude, z, of all points within L could be computed as some (nonlinear) function of x and y. Such an "altitude function" may be determined by finding an n-dimensional polynomial expression of sufficiently high order to separate all the points into two or more groups; the computations required are considerable.

Several alternative solutions to determining the optimal classification rule are possible when optimal discrimination would involve excessive computing time. Approximating a kth order optimal discriminant with some nonlinear discriminant of order lower than k is perhaps the most obvious of these. Sebesteyen offers an interesting example (pp. 69–73) in which a sixth-order polynomial function of two dimensions quite nicely separates a very complex categorization of points on a plane. Since this is quite foreign to the philosophy behind the CLS, where the assumption of ordered values of attributes is denied, we shall not discuss this technique further.

Somewhat more akin to the methods used by the CLS is the technique Sebesteyen refers to as an *adaptive technique*. He considers two types of adaptation. The one with perhaps the longest history is adaptation using a system of continuous adjustment of linear weights. This method has appeared under various names and designs, such as Pandemonium (Selfridge, 1959) and Perceptron (Rosenblatt, 1962). The idea is quite simple. When an object is input it is subjected to a series of tests, for each of which it receives a score. In the most general case scores are either 0 or 1, indicating the presence or absence of a characteristic. Each of the scores is then multiplied by a weight, which may be positive or negative. If the sum of the weighted scores is greater than a certain threshold value the object is assigned to Class A, otherwise it is assigned to Class $-A$. The weights are then readjusted, so that tests which pointed toward the correct answer have their weights increased, while tests which pointed toward the wrong answer have their weights decreased.

Linear weighting schemes differ in how they choose values to assign initial weights and adjust them during problem solving, and in the manner in which the threshold is determined. If the linear weighting schemes are "cascaded," so that the output of one or more linear schemes is combined, complex classification problems can be handled. The linear systems have the added advantage that they form at least a plausible initial step as a model of a biological nerve net (see especially the work of Rosenblatt), but this is not strictly germane to our discussion.

A second generalized adaptive technique discussed by Sebesteyen is the method of classification by reference to the closest cluster of objects. Consider the collection of points in Fig. 9.4. They fall into three classes: circles, plus signs, and the unclassified point indicated by a question mark. The circles and plus signs are not linearly separable; however, the closest occupied point to the unclassified point is a circle. A very simple clustering decision rule would, for this reason, classify the unknown point as a circle.

The simple rule illustrated above is not always the best, as it is subject to random or atypical fluctuations in the locations of objects of different classes. Other clustering rules, such as classifying on the basis of the average distance to all points less than r units from the point representing the unknown object, are also possible. Sebesteyen discusses the various cluster-

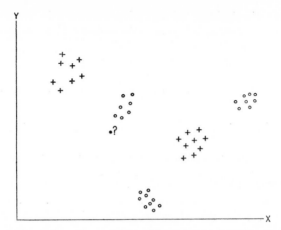

FIG. 9.4. Example of clustering technique. The point marked ? is classified as a circle on the basis of its proximity to a cluster of circles.

ing methods in detail, and shows that they can be used to approximate decision-theoretic methods of classification.

The technique of adaptive adjustment of linear weights and of clustering (which may also be made adaptive by selection of a "good" set of objects on which clusters are to be defined) are best thought of as classes of pattern recognizers, rather than as particular methods of pattern recognition. Different types of linear weighting or clustering schemes are possible, just as different CLS programs are possible within the same general framework.

2. THE FEATURE WORD EXPERIMENTS

A series of experiments on "feature word recognition" have been conducted by Mattson, Firschein, Fischler, and Healy. Since their experiments and methods occupy a sort of way station between the optimal pattern recognition methods discussed by Sebesteyen and the complex tree development of CLS's, and because one of their experiments offers a direct comparison of CLS's with feature word methods, we shall discuss their work in detail.

A *feature word* is defined as a set of binary attributes, e.g., the presence or absence of a particular characteristic, and can be represented by a binary number. For instance, if the objects can be big or small (1 or 0 in the first position), black or white (1 or 0 in the second position), and circles or triangles (1 or 0 in the third position), then all possible combinations can be represented as the vertices of a three dimensional cube, as in Fig. 9.5. Now suppose each object was to be categorized as either "white" or "black," as shown by the circles in Fig. 9.5. In this case the pattern recognition problem is linearly separable, a plane can be passed through the

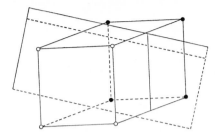

FIG. 9.5. Example of linearly separable pattern recognition problem with feature words.

cube in such a way that the black points are on one side of it, the white points on the other. This is shown in the figure. But suppose that the problem were as shown in Fig. 9.6. This can be solved only by passing *two* planes through the cube, one intersecting the cube at *EF* and at *GH*, the other intersecting at *AB* and *CD*, and classifying the objects as "white points"

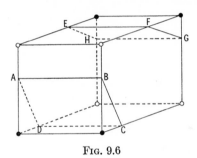

FIG. 9.6

if they lie between the two planes, otherwise classifying the objects as "black points." This is exactly analogous to an "or" branch in a CLS decision tree. In the mathematical sense it is equivalent to having two sets of weights, calculating two thresholds, and defining the description space as consisting of the regions above both thresholds, between them, and below both of them.

We are now in a position to consider briefly the general algorithm for pattern recognition given in Fischler *et al.* (1962). Assume that a set of feature words have been identified and their features recorded, as shown in Table 9.1. The table also indicates a weight vector and a threshold which separates class 1 elements from class 0 elements. Now suppose that the class 1 object 000 is added to the set. The result is shown in Table 9.2. No single threshold suffices to separate 0 and 1 objects. However, if we use two weight sets (indicated in Table 9.2) we may classify objects as class 1 if (a) they have a higher value than 2, using weight set 1, or if (b) they have a lower value than 1, using weight set 2 (i.e., if they are above

TABLE 9.1

FEATURE WORD EXAMPLE SHOWING SINGLE THRESHOLD

Features

Weight vector | 2 | 0 | 1 |

	A	B	C	Class	Wt.
Object	1	1	1	1	3
	1	1	0	1	2
	0	1	1	0	1
	0	1	0	0	0

Threshold = 1

or below the indicated levels T_1 and T_2). Note the similarity of this to a disjunction problem. A CLS would solve this problem as, "Place an object in class 1 (a) if attributes A and B have value 1, or (b) if attribute A and B have value 0.

As is a CLS, the Firschein *et al.* procedure is sequence dependent. If the initial position of a hyperplane is approximately at the position which it

TABLE 9.2

FEATURE WORD EXAMPLE SHOWING TWO THRESHOLDS AND TWO WEIGHT SETS

A	B	C
2	0	1

Weight set 1

A	B	C
1	1	0

Weight set 2

	A	B	C	Class	Wt. (1)	Wt. (2)
	1	1	1	1	3	2
Objects	1	1	0	1	2	2
	0	1	1	0	1	1
	0	1	0	0	0	1
	0	0	0	1	0	0

T1

T2

would be at after the entire universe has been observed, then the development of an accurate classification rule will be rapid. Otherwise, considerable sampling may be required, and an overly complex classification rule may be developed. (This point is covered further by Mattson and Firschein, 1963.)

Mattson *et al.* (1963) have pointed out that pattern recognition problems which are linearly separable (i.e., require a single hyperplane) in an n-dimensional space may be separable by a multiple hyperplane solution in an $n - k$ dimensional space. This corresponds to a solution in which the number of nonzero weights is kept to a minimum. Their experimental results on the recognition of binary patterns of the digits 0–7, with varying amounts of degrading noise added by randomly changing a bit in the binary pattern representing the picture of the number, indicate that, in general, the multiple hyperplane solution is inferior to the n-dimensional single hyperplane solution in this situation. Similar experiments have not been carried out with CLS programs but, presumably, the results would be much the same.

A second experiment (Mattson and Firschein, 1963) involved problems very similar to those used by us. The problems, however, were represented in a rather different framework, and can be used to illustrate both the comparison of the CLS and the feature word system of pattern recognition and to illustrate the importance of selecting a "correct" description space in any pattern recognition system.

The objects on which Mattson and Firschein based their categorization were the integers 0-8192. Any number was expressed as a pattern of ones or zeros, using two different codes. The first code was the conventional expression of a number as sum of increasing powers of two, the familiar binary coding approach. If $N - 1$ is the largest integer, then M, the number of bits required in the code, is the smallest integer equal to or greater than $\log_2 N$. The problem is that the distance between two numbers, numerically, is not reflected by any similarity between the binary patterns used to code them. This can be seen by illustration with $N = 8$. In the second column of Table 9.3 the binary patterns for the integers 0–7 are given.

A simple measure of the distance between the binary patterns is the number of bit positions which have different values. This is called Hamming distance, and corresponds directly to distance in the geometric representation of a binary coding system as, for instance, is shown in Fig. 9.6. The Hamming distance between binary patterns has virtually nothing to do with the numerical difference between integers. For instance, the Hamming distance between the numbers 3 and 4 is 3, while the Hamming distance between 3 and 7 is 1. Thus Hamming distance itself cannot be used as a

TABLE 9.3
BINARY AND LINEAR CODING OF THE INTEGERS 0–7

Integer	Binary coding	Linear coding
0	000	0000000
1	001	0000001
2	010	0000011
3	011	0000111
4	100	0001111
5	101	0011111
6	110	0111111
7	111	1111111

clue to determine class membership if the concept is based upon the numerical value of the integers in each group.

A second manner of coding is shown in the third column of Table 9.3. Mattson and Firschein refer to this as linear coding. The value of the integer is the same as the number of right justified "ones" in the bit pattern; counting proceeds 0, 1, 11, 111, etc. The linear coding system is not nearly as efficient a representation of numbers as the binary in terms of the number of symbols required. On the other hand, the Hamming distance between bit patterns is directly related to the difference between the numerical values of the integers the patterns represent. Thus if distance is a good clue to class membership, one would expect that a pattern recognition system which responded to distance would work better within the (conventionally inefficient) linear scheme. The point in contrasting the two is largely to indicate how the choice of an appropriate description can influence pattern recognition and concept learning. Note that the information upon which a classification rule may be based is present in both coding schemes.

In their experiment, Mattson and Firschein used three number codes of the form ABC, where A was an integer between 0 and 31, and B and C were integers ranging between 0 and 15. Thus we can think of A, B, and C as attributes which could have values. For each attribute, three values were defined. These were as follows:

$$
\begin{array}{llll}
\text{For } A & \text{value 1 } (A_1) & \text{if} & 21 \leqslant A \leqslant 31 \\
 & A_2 & \text{if} & 11 \leqslant A \leqslant 20 \\
 & A_3 & \text{if} & 0 \leqslant A \leqslant 10 \\
\text{For } B, & B_1 & \text{if} & 11 \leqslant B \leqslant 15 \\
 & B_2 & \text{if} & 5 \leqslant B \leqslant 10 \\
 & B_3 & \text{if} & 0 \leqslant B \leqslant 4 \\
\text{For } C, & C_1 & \text{if} & 11 \leqslant C \leqslant 15 \\
 & C_2 & \text{if} & 6 \leqslant C \leqslant 10 \\
 & C_3 & \text{if} & 0 \leqslant C \leqslant 5.
\end{array}
$$

An object was represented by a binary pattern in which the values of A, B, and C were either coded in binary or in linear form. Thus in the linear coded form one could sensibly speak of the Hamming distance along dimensions A, B, and C (but not between them), while this could not be done in the binary coding.

The integers 0–8192 were coded this way by basing A on the value of the five bits of a binary number furthest to the left, B and C on the succeeding four-bit groups. A similar assignment was used for linearly coded numbers.

Mattson and Firschein used 10 problems, representing different Boolean combinations of values of the three attributes, A, B, and C. These are shown in Table 9.4. A word belonged in category 1 (i.e., was a positive instance) if it satisfied the criterion stated in the first column. For instance, in the first problem a feature word was a positive instance if the first number was

TABLE 9.4

COMPARISON OF CLS-1 AND MATTSON AND FIRSCHEIN METHODS[a]

Problem	Binary code		Linear code		CLS results, 50 word sample	
	96 word sample	480 word sample	96 word sample	480 word sample	Problem	Accuracy
$A_1 \cdot B_1 \cdot C_1$	59	84	60	96	2.1	50.2
$A_1 \lor B_1 \lor C_1$	71	—[b]	85	99	2.4	87.8
$A_1 \lor (B_1 \cdot C_1)$	92	—[b]	100	100	2.3	97.0
$A_1 \cdot (B_1 \lor C_1)$	82	—[b]	92	99	2.2	90.5
$A_2 \lor (B_1 \cdot (C_2 \lor C_3))$	55	—[b]	86	99		
$A_2 \cdot C_2 \cdot (B_1 \lor B_3)$	58	—[b]	72	96		
$(A_1 \cdot B_1 \cdot C_1) \lor (A_3 \cdot B_3 \cdot C_3)$	57	—[b]	77	97		
$(A_1 \lor A_2) \cdot (B_3 \cdot C_1)$	64	—[b]	69	92		
$A_2 \lor B_2 \lor C_2$	56	—[b]	62	91	2.4	87.8
$B_2 \cdot ((A_1 \cdot C_3) \lor (A_3 \cdot C_1))$	57	—[b]	83	85		

[a] Figures are % of items correctly identified, adjusted so that chance is 50%.
[b] Data not available.

in the range specified for A_1 and the second number in the range specified for C_1. The hyperplane adjusting program was given either 96 or 480 numbers, in either a binary or linear code, as "known objects." This corresponds to the learning sample in CLS experiments. The percentage of correct identifications for the remaining objects is shown in the body of the table, both for different codings and different sizes of the organizing set.

Certain of the problems resemble those of Problem Set II, which also involve three relevant variables. Actually, Problem Set II is slightly more complicated, since in it objects have three relevant variables with four values per attribute, and also four irrelevant attributes. Since the concept of "distance" is strictly not applicable, Problem Set II is more comparable to binary than linear coding. In the last two columns of Table 9.4 the problem (if any) most similar to the Mattson and Firschein problem is listed, with the performance of CLS-1 using a 50-object learning sample (Experiment III) given in the last column on the right. As can be seen, the accuracy values are quite similar, indicating that the two systems do not differ markedly in their performance. To be sure, the problems are not exactly equivalent, so more testing is necessary. At this point, two quite different pattern recognition systems appear to give identical results. Further comparisons are needed to show the conditions in which one is to be preferred to the other.

3. THE WORK OF UHR AND VOSSLER

The difference between the linear and binary code results obtained by Mattson and Firschein illustrates the importance of having a good description of the objects before the learning phase begins. In CLS experiments the same rules will certainly hold. We have neatly bypassed this problem by assuming that it is solved; by definition the attributes and values have something to do with the concept to be learned. Obviously this assumption has to be made somewhere along the line, since no learning can take place in an environment which the learner cannot sense. The question is to what extent a coding scheme should be imposed upon the primitive "sensation" capability before the concept learning system attempts to assign a design rule. To put the question more closely into the context of research on CLS's and other similar systems: "How should attributes and values be determined?"

A system for pattern recognition which does possess the capability of varying its attributes and value definitions has been designed by Uhr and Vossler (1961, 1963) and applied to a large number of visual pattern recognition problems with considerable success. We describe it here because a fairly straightforward job of combining their system with a CLS program might result in an extremely powerful pattern recognition program.

The input to the Uhr and Vossler program is a pattern of bits. A possible way to think of this is as a two-dimensional matrix of the type shown in Fig. 9.7. This figure shows the letter "A" as it might appear in some scheme of input to a computer. We may think of every "A" as having certain invariant features, such as, for instance, having an inverted "V"-shaped figure at the top, and a nearly horizontal bar somewhere below the inverted "V." This description holds for all "A"s regardless of where they appear on the grid of Fig. 9.7. Now consider the small matrix shown in the lower right of Fig. 9.7. This could be thought of as a "prototype" inverted "V." Any connected area of the larger grid could be selected and the small

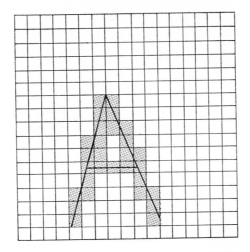

Fig. 9.7. Example of binary pattern of letter "A." The mask in the lower right can be fitted to part of the figure.

matrix fitted to it. If the small matrix matched (or approximately matched) the pattern of ones and zeros in the large matrix, we could say that the small matrix described that region of the large matrix. Uhr and Vossler refer to the small matrix as a local operator, since it is applied to a local region of the larger matrix.

A figure on the large input matrix can be described by stating which local operators fit various parts of the large matrix. This even includes the condition in which the large matrix contains disconnected figures. Relatively simple centering and shrinking or expanding procedures can take care of size and position differences. Formally, we could specify various regions of the large matrix (e.g., upper right-hand corner) as attributes, and let the local operator fitting the region be its value. Equally well, we could call a local operator an "attribute" and the place it fits a "value." In both cases, we would have to allow for the possibility that an attribute might have two values. However, this would provide no insurmountable complications.

The question remains, "Where do the local operators come from?" In many pattern recognition problems (e.g., the recognition of printed characters) the system designer can state, in advance, a set of useful properties. This is essentially what has been done in the CLS programs where we state what the attributes and values are. The Mattson and Firschein results on linear and binary coding indicate the problems that may arise when this advance statement is in error. Uhr and Vossler suggest an efficient procedure for automatic creation of local operators when no advance statement can be made. The essence of their method is imitation of the environment. As their program is shown objects, it randomly selects regions of the input matrix as trial local operators, and copies the patterns of zeros and ones which actually exist for at least one object as a possible operator. Simple statistics are calculated to see whether or not this operator actually proves useful in making discriminations between classes of figures. If it is useful, it is retained as a permanent feature of the coding of the input matrix, but otherwise it is dropped and a new region of the input matrix copied. This scheme has led to reasonably rapid learning of complex discriminations (see particularly Uhr and Vossler, 1963). The Uhr and Vossler program can exceed human performance on a visual pattern recognition task (Uhr *et al.*, 1962).

The Uhr and Vossler method could be used to create attributes and values for CLS programs. In its present form, the program evaluates its local operators by a simple linear weighting scheme which is neither optimal nor presented as such. The results indicate, however, that it is satisfactory and reasonably rapid. It might be possible to make pattern recognition even more rapid by using a CLS decision tree to manipulate the application of local operators. This is particularly attractive, in a situation in which local operators are expensive to apply, since the CLS program would only apply those operators that were to be used in evaluating the particular object under examination.

We have done no experiments using a combined local operator–CLS, but suggest it as a possible topic for future research.

4. RELATION TO ALL-OR-NONE CONCEPT LEARNING

In the following two sections some consideration is given to the role of CLS as a simulation of human problem solving. Again, this is in no sense intended as a survey of the field, since it covers only research which can be related directly to CLS's.

In the past few years a good deal of evidence has been accumulated to show that human simple discrimination learning can be described by an "all-or-none" model. Carefully analyzed data from studies of simple concept learning show that the human subjects do not show any evidence of gradually improving their discrimination learning performance from trial to trial until the last error is made. Instead, they appear suddenly, at a single trial, to "leap" from chance to perfect performance (Estes, 1964). Bower and Trabasso (1963a,b) have further obtained very powerful experimental evidence to show that this is a process of error correction, and that the people learn not by practising the right response in a discrimination situation, but by reordering their hypotheses after wrong ones.

CLS programs are "one-trial learners" in one sense, and gradual learners in another. A CLS program shifts into errorless performance when two events occur: (a) an error is made and the program indicates to itself that the current hypothesis is incorrect and must be destroyed, and (b) sufficient information becomes available to the program to cause it to generate the correct tree. Since the CLS program with infinite memory is psychologically unrealistic, we need consider only systems such as CLS-2, CLS-3, and CLS-9 in which memory is finite.

Before all the spaces in memory are filled, every new object added to the sample has a chance of increasing the number of objects (and hence, the information) available to the program. Since the probability of the program's actually developing the correct tree is an increasing function of the amount of information available to it, CLS's gradually increase their chances of learning up to the point at which memory is full. At this point, assuming that the order in which objects are added to the sample is random, adding an object to the program's memory will always knock out another object. Since the new object is no more likely to contain "key information" than is the object removed from observation, the chance of the CLS having in its memory a configuration of objects which will cause it to generate the correct concept does not increase throughout the remainder of the experiment. (It should be noted that it is possible to create a problem which is so complex that the CLS program cannot hold such a configuration of objects in its memory, and hence cannot solve the problem owing to "poor immediate memory." A loose psychological analogy is obvious.) As a result, a CLS program with finite memory size can be described as being a gradual learner up until the point at which its memory is filled, and an all-or-none learner thereafter.

A word of caution is in order concerning this comparison. The experimental evidence for the "all-or-none" model of human learning rests almost entirely on the learning of very simple concepts, such as "red" vs. "blue." In fact, such experiments involve more the identification of concepts that the subject already has than they do the concatenation of a new concept from old ones. Whether the all-or-none model would hold for the learning of complex disjunctions is, at present, unknown. We have recently obtained some evidence indicating that the entire solution of a complex problem is not reached on a single trial, but that the solution process does consist of the learning of subproblems on an all-or-none basis (Crawford *et al.*, 1965). The experimental evidence at present, however, is not sufficiently reliable to warrant any firm conclusions.

5. THE EPAM MODEL OF VERBAL LEARNING

Feigenbaum (1961) has developed an information processing model of paired-associates learning which is superficially similar to the CLS technique, but which differs from it in some important ways. Since both Feigenbaum's Elementary Perceiving And Memorizing (EPAM) program and the CLS techniques developed from the work of Newell *et al.* (1958) on computer models of complex mental processes, the similarities and differences between the EPAM and CLS approaches are worth comment.

Feigenbaum is concerned with the process by which one nonsense syllable becomes the stimulus for another in rote learning situations, such as the paired-associates and serial-learning paradigms (McGeoch and Irion, 1952). He has also speculated about ways in which a simulation of these situations might represent more complex tasks, such as reading or language translation. These speculations are quite difficult to translate into experimental tests, though they may well be correct. In Feigenbaum's models the stimuli and responses are regarded as collections of symbols. The symbols could represent letters, e.g., J-A-X, phonemes, parts of letters (i.e., J is a straight vertical line above a hook, requiring two symbols) or any other cue which the experimenter thought was relevant. What these symbols are is a question which Feigenbaum need not answer, since he is concerned with the manipulation of symbols within a term after the symbols have been defined "inside the subject." For ease of exposition, we will regard a consonant-vowel-consonant nonsense (CVC) syllable as a set of letters, each letter being identified by its position.

The EPAM model distinguishes between syllables by assigning to each syllable a unique position in a discrimination tree. Stored with every stimulus term in the discrimination tree is a map of the route from the root of the tree to the response term appropriate for that stimulus term. What this means is best shown by a simple example. Consider the following list of paired associates:

Stimulus	*Response*
JAR	BIL
JOP	BEG

This list can be represented by the discrimination tree shown in Fig. 9.8. Each endpoint in the tree corresponds to a particular CVC nonsense syllable. The "route" from stimulus to response is stored with each stimulus term. Thus (RR) stored with JOP indicates that by going right and then right again from the root of the tree, the response term for JOP, BEG, can be reached.

EPAM begins with a simple tree of perhaps two or three pairs. New terms are added to the tree, and new discriminations are placed in it as

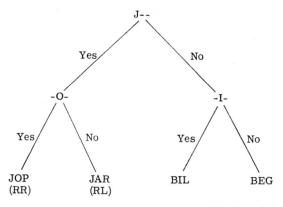

FIG. 9.8. A simple discrimination tree using the EPAM technique.

necessary. Since the map from stimulus to response is stored with the stimulus at the time of original entry, the map may be incorrect if the stimulus or response term is moved because similar items have been introduced since the pair was originally placed in the tree. EPAM also contains other features, such as a "noticing order" for letter positions, provision for order of selection of pairs to be learned, and further definitions of stimulus and response terms. However, the simple exposition given here should be sufficient to make the point.

The published reports show that EPAM "learns" a paired-associates or serial list by establishing a discrimination tree containing the necessary information about the order in which responses must follow stimuli. The failures of discrimination which EPAM makes while trying out trees will mirror, at least at the qualitative level, the phenomena of response interference, retroactive interference, and stimulus and response generalization. When the model is compared to specific experiments (Simon and Feigenbaum, 1965) a reasonably good correspondence is obtained.[1]

---

[1] EPAM is very difficult to test because, in spite of its name, the perceiving mechanism is arbitrary. The stimulus is regarded as a series of "chunks," perceptual units which are the code that the subject uses to represent the stimulus to himself. This is a very reasonable position, with a good deal of evidence to support it (Miller, 1956). In fact, any memory system, human or artificial, has to represent the stimulus in this way (Hunt, 1963). Having assumed the "chunks," EPAM provides a very clever and sophisticated technique of tying chunks together into stimuli. This technique could be a completely accurate representation of how the subject handled the encoded stimuli and at the same time a completely useless model for predicting responses because the assumption about the encoding process was wrong. For example, in his early work Feigenbaum (1961) used the visual characteristics of letters. This is almost certainly in error, nonsense syllables are probably represented internally by their sound, instead of their appearance (Underwood and Schulz, 1960). EPAM can, and has, been corrected

To our knowledge, EPAM has not been used to simulate a concept learning experiment, but to do so does not seem to be particularly difficult. All that is needed is to have more than one stimulus term associated with each response term. For example, consider the modification of a paired-associates experiment to a concept learning experiment by the following pairing:

Stimulus	*Response*
JAD	BIL
TOD	BER
JEP	BIL
TAD	BER

An EPAM type of tree for this matching appears on the left side of Fig. 9.9; a CLS type of tree corresponding to it is on the right. These trees illustrate the basic difference between CLS and EPAM simulations.

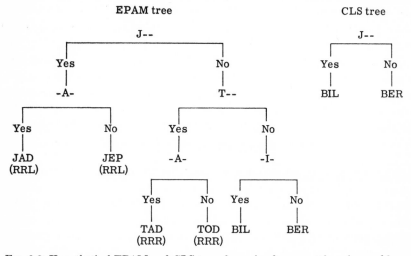

Fig. 9.9. Hypothetical EPAM and CLS trees for a simple concept learning problem.

EPAM's form a categorizing rule by pairwise discrimination, while CLS's respond to similarities within and differences between sets of objects. Although superficially similar, the two programs actually work on opposed

to remedy this (Feigenbaum and Simon, 1963; Simon and Feigenbaum, 1964). But as soon as we get away from nonsense syllables entirely different encoding processes, such as responses to meaning, come into play. The point is *not* that EPAM is a bad model, or a useless model because it does not contain a perceptual process, but that it is inherently a very difficult model to test because we do not know how to predict the subject's description of the stimuli. EPAM, CLS's, and in fact all learning models face the same difficulty. Perception must be controlled before tests of learning can be conducted.

logics. The EPAM method could be modified to handle concept learning, while it is not clear how a CLS could be modified to handle paired-associates learning. It is doubtful, however, whether any modification that retained the basic logic of the EPAM model would produce a realistic simulation of concept learning. Since discrimination is pairwise, the addition of further pairs, such as

Stimulus	Response
JIB	BIL
TAK	BER

would complicate the EPAM tree, while a CLS tree would remain unchanged. This is because the complexity of an EPAM tree increases with the number of items to be discriminated. This is appropriate in simulating paired-associates learning, as there is an increase in task difficulty as list length increases. In concept learning increasing the number of pairs, while keeping the number of response terms and the complexity of the concept constant, either has no effect on the task or makes it easier (Reed, 1946; Smith *et al.*, 1963).

The fact that list length has different effects in the concept learning and paired-associates task, taken together with the fact that generalization between stimuli appears to play a different part in each situation (Shepard *et al.*, 1961), suggests that different psychological processes are involved and that one simulation ought not to be expected to cover both fields.

6. EVALUATION OF CLS'S

Determining whether or not a specific CLS program is a simulation of human performance in a given situation is a straightforward procedure. One performs the relevant experiment and compares the simulation to the data. It is almost certain that no one CLS program will be found to mimic human behavior in every concept learning situation. The more realistic question is whether or not it is possible to be sufficiently accurate in specific situations and sufficiently general so that the model can be used to account for different experiments. Some sort of trade off between accuracy and generality is bound to occur. Whether a particular model is "confirmed" or "rejected" by a certain experiment does not seem to be the point. A more meaningful approach is to ask, "Is this model more accurate in accounting for interesting behavior than any other model"? Such an approach is essentially a Bayesian decision procedure, and whether or not one goes on with the investigation of CLS stimulation depends on the utility one assigns to particular measures of accuracy and to the alternate models which one has under consideration. This is not a counsel of despair, since eventually everyone investigating particular phenomena should converge on the same explanation. Until they reach this convergence point, however, there may be honest disagreement as to which model is "ahead," since this will depend on the idiosyncratic biases of the individual psychologist.

When we look at the use of CLS's as artificial intelligence devices quite another type of evaluation is in order. Any data processing technique, from the computation of a mean to the application of a CLS program, is a device for reducing data. Some of these devices contain within them convenient statistical tests to see if the results obtained are different from those which would be obtained if some uninteresting model (e.g., the null hypothesis) were to be applied to the same data. Today, no such tests exist for use with CLS programs. Any CLS technique will always produce a tree, any data which can be described to a CLS program has at least one and possibly very many trees which can be used to recreate the dichotomy of positive and negative instances.

The fact that we cannot test CLS results against some well-defined "chance" level does not mean that we should reject the approach. In the first place, the statement that we do not know how to make such a test is quite different from the statement that such a test cannot be constructed. Further, there is a good precedent for plunging ahead without waiting for the development of statistical tests. Consider the case of factor analysis. Today one can use any of several factor-analytic techniques, getting different answers depending on the technique used. A given answer may be evaluated against the "chance expectation" (Harmon, 1960), but this was not always the case. When factor analysis was first proposed it was a method for producing one of an infinite number of reductions of scaled data, any of which could be fitted into the general factor-analytic model. After a great deal of experimentation it was found that certain types of factor-analytic procedures tended to produce pictures of the data which were highly useful. These procedures were used to develop further tests. This is not a criticism, it is a description of a rational way of doing things.

CLS programs can be looked upon as similar techniques when the data is composed of discrete descriptions, i.e., attribute-value pairs instead of ordinal measurements. In order to make a rational choice of which CLS to use one needs to know how different variations internal to the program will interact with possible structures of the data. One may also want to know, in a rather loose fashion, the effects of using particular CLS programs in situations which resemble the problem at hand. This chapter has described one "field report" of the method; other such studies are in progress. Finally, one must be careful to remember that the results obtained are strictly limited to the CLS program he used and are also subject to any general limitations of the CLS approach. Exactly the same caution is applicable to the use of any experimental report.

Factor-analytic techniques have developed far beyond their original formulation. CLS techniques could be similarly developed. Would this be worthwhile? At this point, who can tell? Analysis of data which can only be represented by nominal scales is currently performed in only a simple fashion. Sophisticated techniques have not been constructed because the sheer amount of computation they require has been thought to rule them out as practical data processors. With the advent of digital computers, this excuse for simple treatment of data is no longer valid. Our most optimistic view of CLS techniques would be exceeded if they turn out to be the complement to factor analysis for nominal data. Their development will have served its purpose if it leads to this.

Computations in CLS Programs

1. NOTATION AND CONVENTIONS

1.1 General

This appendix states the detailed computations required for each of the algorithms involved in the various concept learning systems. The notational scheme used was developed by Iverson (1962). Only trivial deviations from his original proposals have been introduced. They are generally similar to changes proposed by Iverson (1964) in a subsequent report.

In Section 1 the basic conventions and symbols are introduced. Much of this discussion is taken from the appendix "Summary of notation" in Iverson's book. In Section 2 some special data structures useful in discussing concept learning problems are defined. In Section 3 the detailed algorithms are stated.

Every effort possible has been made to insure that the algorithms are defined correctly. Ideally, this would have been done by writing subroutines equivalent to each of the operations in the Iverson programming language, and testing the CLS algorithms by concatenating them into an actual compiler program in the manner indicated by the algorithm. In practice, the reverse has been done. The programs were written first and then translated back to the Iverson notation. This was necessary simply because the programs predated publication of Iverson's notation. Even so, the ideal solution would have been to check on the translation by reprogramming each CLS from its representation in Iverson notation. This would have required a great deal of time which just was not available. The translations have been checked as carefully as possible by proofreading and by logical analysis, but they have not been subjected to mechanical verification by the computer. Therefore, they should be regarded as a guide to the computations we have used. Hopefully, they are a completely accurate statement. As any experienced programmer knows, this is a very optimistic hope.

1.2 Iverson notation

CONVENTIONS

(1)   Indexing begins at 1 unless otherwise noted.

(2)(a)   Variables are indicated by lower case letters; a, b, c, ...

(b)   Vectors are indicated by lower case italics; a, b, c, ...

(c)   Where necessary to avoid confusion, the dimension of a vector is indicated in parentheses. Thus a(b) states that a is a vector of dimension b. Dimensionality is not specifically indicated if it is obvious from context.

(d)   Matrices are indicated by upper case boldface; **A, B,** . . . .

(e)   Columns and rows of matrices are indicated respectively by subscripts and superscripts. For example, $\mathbf{A}_j^i$ is the entry in the ith column and jth row of matrix **A**.

(3)(a)   Specification statements are indicated by left arrows. The statement a $\longleftarrow$ b indicates that variable a is set equal to the value of variable b.

(b)   The specification a $\longleftrightarrow$ b is interpreted as being equivalent to the following sequence, which sets a equal to the original value of b, and b to the original value of a:

$$c \longleftarrow a$$
$$a \longleftarrow b$$
$$b \longleftarrow c$$

(4)(a)   Unless otherwise indicated, statements are listed vertically, numbered, and executed in that order.

(b)   The colon (:) separating two numbers (e.g., x:y) indicates a comparison between them.

(c)   The branching arrow with relation, attached to a comparison statement in the fashion

$$\overset{R}{|x:y| \longrightarrow}$$

indicates that if the relation xRy is satisfied the arrow points to the next statement to be executed. More than one arrow may lead from a statement. If there is no arrow leading from a statement for which the relation xRy is satisfied the next statement in order is to be executed.

(d)   An unlabeled arrow (no relation) following a specification statement indicates an unconditional change in the normal sequence of control.

STRUCTURAL PARAMETERS

(1) $v(a)$ Number of components (dimensionality) of a.

(2) $v(\mathbf{A})$ Row dimensionality of **A**.

(3) $u(\mathbf{A})$ Column dimensionality of $\mathbf{A}$.

(4) $\bigcirc$ The null symbol.

RELATIONAL AND ARITHMETIC OPERATORS

(1) Normal arithmetic and relational operators (e.g., $a + b$) have their usual meaning. A precise definition of each arithmetic operator is given by Iverson (1962, p. 267).

(2) The following special operations are defined:

(a) $k \leftarrow \lfloor x$ $k \leq x \leq k + 1$.

(b) $k \leftarrow \lceil x$ $k \geq x > k - 1$.

(c) $j \leftarrow \lfloor a$ j is set equal to the minimum valued component of a.

(d) $j \leftarrow \lceil a$ j is set equal to the maximum valued component of a.

VECTOR OPERATIONS

(1) $c \leftarrow a \odot b$ $\odot$ is an elementary operation (addition, subtraction, etc.):

$c_i \leftarrow a_i \odot b_i$

(2) $b \leftarrow x \, a$ Scalar multiplication:

$b_i \leftarrow x \cdot a_i$

(3) $a \leftarrow \odot b$ Reduction

$a \leftarrow (((b_1 \odot b_2) \odot b_3) \odot b_4 \cdots)$

(4) $c \leftarrow u/a$ Compression. All elements of u are either zero or one. c is obtained from a by the following process: if $u_i = 0$, a_i is dropped, if $u_i = 1$, a_i is appended to c as defined thus far. For example,

$c \leftarrow (1, 0, 0, 1)/(2, 9, 3, 6)$

$c = (2, 6)$.

(5) $c \leftarrow u \backslash a$ Expansion. $\bar{u}/c = 0$, $u/c = a$.

(6) $c \leftarrow \backslash a, u, b \backslash$ Mesh. $\bar{u}/c = a$, $u/c = b$.

(7) $c \leftarrow a \oplus b$ Catenation. $c \leftarrow (a_i \cdots a_n), (b_1 \cdots b_m)$

(8) $c \leftarrow / a, u, b /$ Mask. $\bar{u}/c = \bar{u}/a$, $u/c = u/b$

(9) $w \leftarrow \epsilon_y^x$ $w_i = (y_i \, \epsilon \, x)$, $v(w) = v(y)$

(10) $w \leftarrow \epsilon^j(h)$ $w_i = (i = j)$, $v(w) = h$

(11) $w \leftarrow \epsilon(h)$ $w_i = 1$ $v(w) = h$

(12) $w \leftarrow \bar{\epsilon}(h)$ $w_i = 0$ $v(w) = h$

(13) $w \leftarrow \alpha^j(h)$ First j items of w are 1, remaining are 0. $v(w) = h$

(14) $w \leftarrow \omega^j(h)$ Last j items of w are 1, remaining are 0. $v(w) = h$

(15) $w \leftarrow \alpha/u$ w = maximum length prefix in u. For example,

$$/(1, 1, 0, 1, 0, 1) = (1, 1, 0, 0, 0, 0).$$

(16) $w \leftarrow \omega/u$ w = maximum length suffix in u.

GENERALIZATION OF MATRIX OPERATIONS TO VECTORS

(1) $c \leftarrow \odot/\mathbf{A}$ $c_i \leftarrow \odot/\mathbf{A}_i$ generalizes all vector operations (row generalization).

(2) $c \leftarrow \odot//\mathbf{A}$ $c_j \leftarrow \odot/\mathbf{A}_j$ (column generalization).

SPECIAL LOGICAL MATRICES

(1) $\mathbf{W} \leftarrow \bar{\mathbf{E}}(p, q)$ $\mathbf{W}_j^i = 1$, $u(\mathbf{W}) = p$, $v(\mathbf{W}) = q$.
(2) $\mathbf{W} \leftarrow \mathbf{E}$ $\mathbf{W}_j^i = 0$.
(3) $\mathbf{I}$ The identity matrix, $\mathbf{I}_j^i = (i = j)$.

2. SPECIAL DEFINITIONS USED IN DISCUSSING CONCEPT LEARNING

2.1 Attributes (Chapter 1, Sections 2 and 3):

(1) a_i is a column vector, the ordered set of values of attribute i.
(2) $\mathbf{A}$ = Attribute-value matrix.

$\mathbf{A}_i = a_i \oplus \bigcirc \epsilon$.

$u(\mathbf{A})$ = Maximum number of values of any attribute.

$v(\mathbf{A})$ = Total number of attributes.

$\mathbf{A}_i^j = jth$ value of attribute i,

  $= j$ if $v(a_i) \geqslant j$.

  $= \bigcirc$ if $v(a_i) < j$.

2.2 Descriptions (Chapter 1, Section 3)

(1) d^k Description of object k
(2) d_j^k Value of attribute j for object k
(3) $\mathbf{D}$ Description matrix stating full form description of a concept.

$v(\mathbf{D}) = n + 1$, one plus number of attributes.

$u(\mathbf{D}) = m$, total number of descriptions in universe.

(4) $\mathbf{D}_j^k = d_j^k$ if $j \leqslant n$.

$\mathbf{D}_{n+1}^k = 1$ if object k is a positive instance, 0 otherwise.

(5) c^g = Vector specifying gth subset of the set of possible descriptions.

(6) $c_j^g = \mathbf{A}_j^i$ if all objects in set g have value i of attribute j.

          $-\mathbf{A}_j^i$ if no objects in set g have value i of attribute j.

          $\bigcirc$ if the value of attribute j is not specified for objects in set g.

(7) c_{n+1}^g = 1 if all objects in set g are positive instances
         0 if no objects in set g are positive instances. Set g is
         erroneously defined if one of these two statements does
         not hold.

2.3 Trees (Chapter 1, Sections 4 and 5)

(1) **T** = A matrix of dimensions $v(\mathbf{T}) = n + 2$, $u(\mathbf{T})$ arbitrary, used
         to represent a tree. Nodes are indexed by rows.

(2) $\mathbf{T}_i^j$, $3 \le i \le n$, $= s \,\epsilon\, a^i$ or $\bigcirc$ if node j is a test node
         = 0 if node j is an endpoint.

(3) $\mathbf{T}_1^j$ $= s \,\epsilon\, a^1$ or $\bigcirc$ if node j is a testpoint;
         $= -1$ if node j is an endpoint.

(4) $\mathbf{T}_2^j$ = 1 if the jth node is a positive endpoint;
         = 0 if the jth node is a negative endpoint;
         $= s \,\epsilon\, a^2$ or $\bigcirc$ if the jth node is a testpoint.

(5) $\mathbf{T}_{n+1}^j$ $= k \le u(\mathbf{T})$, the left successor node j, if j is a
         test node.
         = 0 if the jth node is an endpoint.

(6) $\mathbf{T}_{n+2}^j$ $= m \le u(\mathbf{T})$, the right successor of node j, if the
         jth node is a testpoint.
         = 0 if the jth node is an endpoint.

Notes: (a) In Iverson's terminology, the left successor would be called the
heir, and the right successor the successor.

(b) Graphical representations corresponding to the matrix definitions are given in Section 1.5.

3. PROGRAMS

3.1 Classification Program

DESCRIPTION

T is a tree and $\mathbf{D}^i$ a vector in the form of a row of a description matrix.
$\mathbf{D}^i$ is passed through **T** until an endpoint is reached. The variable e is set
equal to the index of the endpoint. The variable c is set equal to one if the
endpoint correctly classifies the description, zero otherwise.

CANONICAL FORM

e, c $\leftarrow$ classify $(\mathbf{T}, \mathbf{D}^i)$

PROGRAM

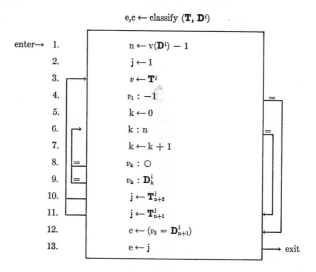

$$e, c \leftarrow \text{classify } (\mathbf{T}, \mathbf{D}^i)$$

enter→ 1.	$n \leftarrow v(\mathbf{D}^i) - 1$
2.	$j \leftarrow 1$
3.	$v \leftarrow \mathbf{T}^j$
4.	$v_1 : -1$
5.	$k \leftarrow 0$
6.	$k : n$
7.	$k \leftarrow k + 1$
8.	$v_k : \bigcirc$
9.	$v_k : \mathbf{D}_k^i$
10.	$j \leftarrow \mathbf{T}_{n+2}^j$
11.	$j \leftarrow \mathbf{T}_{n+1}^j$
12.	$c \leftarrow (v_2 = \mathbf{D}_{n+1}^i)$
13.	$e \leftarrow j$

PROGRAM 1. Routine for classification.

Program 1, classification routine. In this and all subsequent programs the function $j \leftarrow \text{random } (i)$ is understood to assign to j as a randomly chosen integer in the interval $1 - - i$ inclusive.

3.2   Sample Selection Programs

GENERAL COMMENTS

A sample matrix is a matrix whose rows specify the items available to the CLS. A description matrix, **D**, specifies candidates for the sample matrix **S**.

SAMPLE 1 PROGRAM, DESCRIPTION

A fixed number, k, of rows are chosen at random from **D**, without replacement, and placed in **S** in order of choice. The number of attributes is understood to be n.

CANONICAL FORM OF SAMPLE 1 PROGRAM

$\mathbf{S} \leftarrow \text{sample } 1 \; (\mathbf{D}, k)$

PROGRAM

Program 2.

$$\mathbf{S} \leftarrow \text{sample 1 } (\mathbf{D}, \text{k})$$

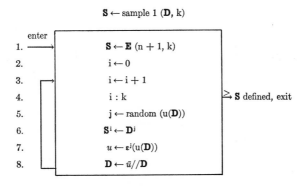

PROGRAM 2. Sample 1 program.

SAMPLE 2 PROGRAM DESCRIPTION

Given a description, matrix **D**, an entry controller, q, an index, t, and a sample matrix of column dimension $t - 1$ (thus containing description of $t - 1$ items), this program sets t*th* row of **S** equal to that row of **D** which shares the most common valued attributes with row $t - 1$ of **S**, providing that q = 0. If $q \neq 0$ $\mathbf{S}^t$ is chosen randomly from **D**. In either case the chosen row of **D** is removed from **D**.

CANONICAL FORM

$$\mathbf{S} \leftarrow \text{sample 2 } (\mathbf{S}, \mathbf{D}, \text{q}, \text{t})$$

PROGRAM

$$\mathbf{S} \leftarrow \text{sample 2 } (\mathbf{S}, \mathbf{D}, q, t)$$

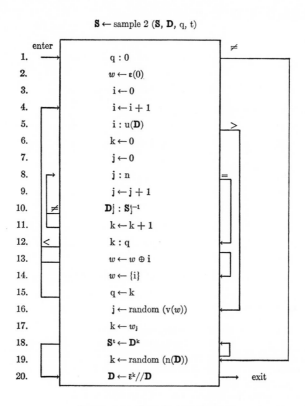

PROGRAM 3. Sample 2 program.

SAMPLE 3 PROGRAM DESCRIPTION

The entry variables are $\mathbf{S}$, $\mathbf{D}$, and q (with definitions as for the sample 2 program), a tree, $\mathbf{T}$, and an endpoint, e*, of $\mathbf{T}$. If q = 0 the rows of $\mathbf{D}$ are examined in order, routed through $\mathbf{T}$, and the first one which reaches endpoint e* is removed from $\mathbf{D}$ and added to $\mathbf{S}$. If no such row is found or if q = 1 a row is chosen randomly from $\mathbf{D}$.

$\mathbf{S} \leftarrow$ sample 3 $(\mathbf{S}, \mathbf{D}, \mathbf{T}, e^*, q)$

Program

Program 4.

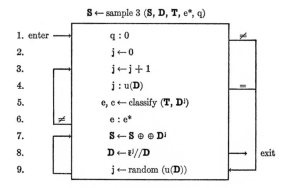

$\mathbf{S} \leftarrow$ sample 3 $(\mathbf{S}, \mathbf{D}, \mathbf{T}, e^*, q)$

1. enter	$q : 0$	$\neq$
2.	$j \leftarrow 0$	
3.	$j \leftarrow j + 1$	
4.	$j : u(\mathbf{D})$	$=$
5.	$e, c \leftarrow$ classify $(\mathbf{T}, \mathbf{D}^j)$	
6.	$e : e^*$	
7.	$\mathbf{S} \leftarrow \mathbf{S} \oplus \oplus \mathbf{D}^j$	
8.	$\mathbf{D} \leftarrow \mathbf{e}^j // \mathbf{D}$	exit
9.	$j \leftarrow$ random $(u(\mathbf{D}))$	

Program 4. Sample 3 program.

3.3 Memory Programs

Memory 1 (Direct Copy)—Description

Rows from the sample matrix $\mathbf{S}$ are copied, in order, directly into the memory matrix $\mathbf{M}$. There is no provision for dropping items previously read.

Canonical Form

$\mathbf{M}^i \leftarrow$ memory 1 $(\mathbf{S})$

Program

Program 5.

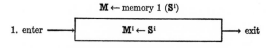

$\mathbf{M} \leftarrow$ memory 1 $(\mathbf{S}^i)$

1. enter $\longrightarrow$ $\mathbf{M}^i \leftarrow \mathbf{S}^i$ $\longrightarrow$ exit

Program 5. Memory 1 program.

Memory 2 (Random Storage)—Description

Given s, the maximum size of the memory matrix, and a matrix $\mathbf{M}$ of column dimension d, $d \leq s$, the first row of $\mathbf{S}$ is removed from $\mathbf{S}$ and, depending on the value of a random integer $0 < j \leq s$, is either added to **M** (if $j > d$) or replaces the j*th* row of **M** (if $j \leq d$). In the first case the column dimension of **M** is increased by one.

CANONICAL FORM

$M \leftarrow$ memory 2 (**S**, s, **M**)

PROGRAM

Program 6.

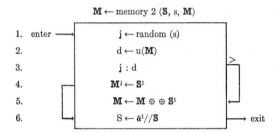

PROGRAM 6. Memory 2 program.

MEMORY 3 (RANDOM STORAGE IN SPECIFIC AREAS)—DESCRIPTION

M is composed of two separate memory matrices, **M+** and **M−**, each of maximum column dimension $\frac{1}{2}$s (s is assumed to be an integer). If the first row of the sample matrix describes a positive instance ($\mathbf{S}^1_{n+1} = 1$) this row is added to **M+** using the memory 2 program. Otherwise the row is stored in **M−**. **M+** and **M−** are then catenated to form **M**.

CANONICAL FORM

M ← memory 3 (**S**, s, **M+**, **M−**).

PROGRAM

Program 7.

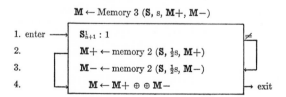

PROGRAM 7. Memory 3 program.

3.4   The Wholist Algorithm

DESCRIPTION

Given a sample matrix S, a tree, T, and an index, i, S is examined to see if a conjunctive concept can be used to classify the items in S. If such a concept can be found it is stated as a one test node, two endpoint tree with its root at i (thus the tree becomes a subtree of T). A marker variable, q, is set equal to 1 if a conjunctive concept can be found, otherwise the marker variable is set equal to 0 and T is not changed. There is an implicit change in T if q = 1 at the end of the program. The program is defined for a sample matrix or for any other matrix (e.g., a memory matrix) whose rows have the same form as those of a sample matrix.

CANONICAL FORM

T, q $\leftarrow$ wholist (S, T, i)

PROGRAM

Program 8.

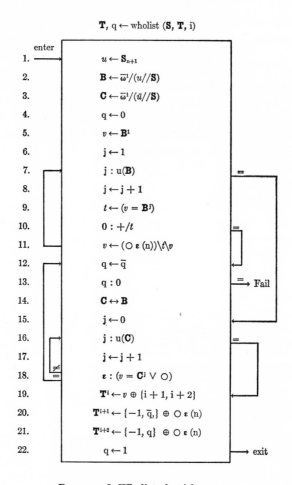

$$\mathbf{T}, q \leftarrow \text{wholist } (\mathbf{S}, \mathbf{T}, i)$$

enter
1. $u \leftarrow \mathbf{S}_{n+1}$
2. $\mathbf{B} \leftarrow \bar{\omega}^1/(u//\mathbf{S})$
3. $\mathbf{C} \leftarrow \bar{\omega}^1/(\bar{u}//\mathbf{S})$
4. $q \leftarrow 0$
5. $v \leftarrow \mathbf{B}^1$
6. $j \leftarrow 1$
7. $j : u(\mathbf{B})$
8. $j \leftarrow j + 1$
9. $t \leftarrow (v = \mathbf{B}^j)$
10. $0 : +/t$
11. $v \leftarrow (\bigcirc \varepsilon (n)) \backslash t \backslash v$
12. $q \leftarrow \bar{q}$
13. $q : 0$
14. $\mathbf{C} \leftrightarrow \mathbf{B}$
15. $j \leftarrow 0$
16. $j : u(\mathbf{C})$
17. $j \leftarrow j + 1$
18. $\varepsilon : (v = \mathbf{C}^j \vee \bigcirc)$
19. $\mathbf{T}^i \leftarrow v \oplus \{i + 1, i + 2\}$
20. $\mathbf{T}^{i+1} \leftarrow \{-1, \bar{q},\} \oplus \bigcirc \varepsilon (n)$
21. $\mathbf{T}^{i+2} \leftarrow \{-1, q\} \oplus \bigcirc \varepsilon (n)$
22. $q \leftarrow 1$

→ Fail

→ exit

PROGRAM 8. Wholist algorithm.

3.5 Selection Programs

GENERAL

These programs define procedures for selecting tests at a node when the wholist algorithm fails.

MAXIMUM FREQUENCY SELECTION PROGRAM DESCRIBED

Given a sample matrix, **S**, this program selects the attribute a, and the value, v, of the characteristic which has the highest frequency of occurrence on positive instances in the sample described by **S**.

CANONICAL FORM

a, v ← maxslct (**S**)

PROGRAM

Program 9.

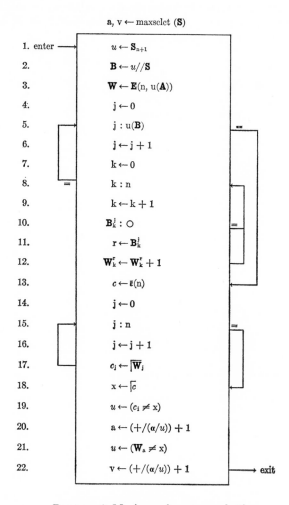

PROGRAM 9. Maximum frequency selection.

SUBTRACTION SELECTION PROGRAM DESCRIBED.

Given a sample matrix, **S**, this program selects an attribute a, with value v, such that the quantity equal to the frequency of occurrence of this characteristic on positive instances minus the frequency of occurrence on negative instances is maximized.

CANONICAL FORM

a, v ← subslct (**S**)

PROGRAM

Program 10.

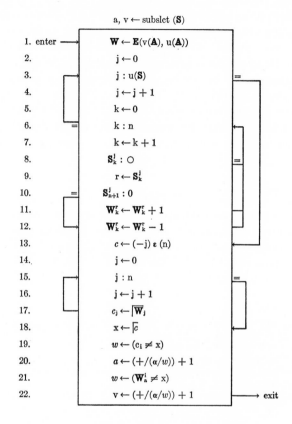

PROGRAM 10. Selection by subtraction criterion.

3.6 Concept Learning System Programs

GENERAL

Each of these programs defines a particular CLS. The computations of
each system are defined in terms of the previously presented programs.
Each system consists of two sections, a *main program* and a *solution
program*. The main program arranges the sample, arranges memory, and
checks the correctness of the current concept. The solution program
develops a new concept when required. Since several systems use the same
program, some of the system computations are defined by specifying their
change from previously stated systems, rather than by repeating the entire
program. This is done under the "program" heading of each system
description.

CLS-1 MAIN PROGRAM, DESCRIPTION

Given a description space, **D**, and an integer, k, specifying the maximum
size of the sample, this program establishes a concept by sequential examination of the first k randomly chosen descriptions. A perfect memory
system with assumed infinite storage is used. The *maxslct* computation is
used to define subproblems when necessary.

CANONICAL FORM

$\mathbf{T} \leftarrow$ CLS-1 $(\mathbf{D}, k)$

PROGRAM

Program 11.

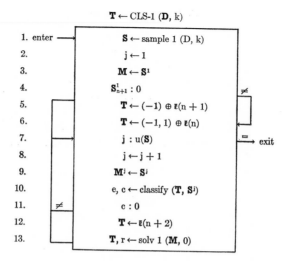

PROGRAM 11. CLS-1 main program. (*solv 1*, used in line 13, is defined by Program 12.)

CLS-1 SOLUTION ROUTINE (SOLV 1) DESCRIPTION

Given a sample matrix **S** (or equivalent memory matrix), a tree, **T**, and an index, j, indicating the node to be regarded as the root of a tree or subtree, the program develops a subtree, rooted at node j, which can be used to classify the items in **S**. The *maxslct* computation is used to define subproblems while the tree is being developed. The program returns **T**, modified by the addition of the subtree beginning at node j, and a new value of j indicating the index of the last endpoint of the subtree. This is necessary for proper recursive definition of the program.

CANONICAL FORM

T, j ← solv 1 (**S**, **T**, j)

PROGRAM

Program 12.

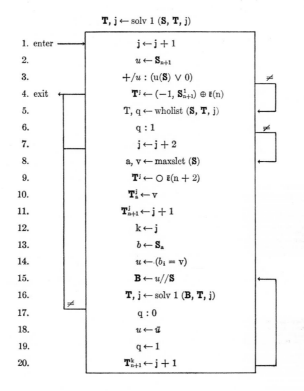

$$\mathbf{T}, j \leftarrow \text{solv 1} \ (\mathbf{S}, \mathbf{T}, j)$$

1. enter	$j \leftarrow j + 1$
2.	$u \leftarrow \mathbf{S}_{n+1}$
3.	$+/u : (u(\mathbf{S}) \vee 0)$
4. exit	$\mathbf{T}^j \leftarrow (-1, \mathbf{S}^1_{n+1}) \oplus \bar{\varepsilon}(n)$
5.	$\mathbf{T}, q \leftarrow \text{wholist} \ (\mathbf{S}, \mathbf{T}, j)$
6.	$q : 1$
7.	$j \leftarrow j + 2$
8.	$a, v \leftarrow \text{maxslct} \ (\mathbf{S})$
9.	$\mathbf{T}^j \leftarrow \bigcirc \bar{\varepsilon}(n + 2)$
10.	$\mathbf{T}^j_a \leftarrow v$
11.	$\mathbf{T}^j_{n+1} \leftarrow j + 1$
12.	$k \leftarrow j$
13.	$b \leftarrow \mathbf{S}_a$
14.	$u \leftarrow (b_i = v)$
15.	$\mathbf{B} \leftarrow u // \mathbf{S}$
16.	$\mathbf{T}, j \leftarrow \text{solv 1} \ (\mathbf{B}, \mathbf{T}, j)$
17.	$q : 0$
18.	$u \leftarrow \bar{u}$
19.	$q \leftarrow 1$
20.	$\mathbf{T}^k_{n+1} \leftarrow j + 1$

PROGRAM 12. Definition of solv 1 subroutine.

CLS-2 AND CLS-3

These programs are identical to CLS-1 except that an additional control parameter, s, is inserted to indicate the maximum size of memory. In CLS-2 the memory 2 program is used to define the actual contents of memory at any one time, in CLS-2 memory 3 is used.

CANONICAL FORMS

$\mathbf{T} \leftarrow$ CLS-2 ($\mathbf{D}$, k, s)
$\mathbf{T} \leftarrow$ CLS-3 ($\mathbf{D}$, k, s)

PROGRAMS

The main programs are identical to the main routine for CLS-1 (Program 11) except that in CLS-2 the statement "$\mathbf{M} \leftarrow$ memory 2 ($\mathbf{S}$, s, $\mathbf{M}$)" replaces line 9, while in CLS-3 the statement "$\mathbf{M} \leftarrow$ memory 3 ($\mathbf{S}$, s, $\mathbf{M}$)" replaces line 9.

The solution routine used is *solv 1*, Program 12.

CLS-4 DESCRIPTION

CLS-4 differs from CLS-1 only in the manner of choosing a sample. The solution routine is *solv 1*. The sample is defined by using program *sample 2* to select the sequence of items to be presented to the system.

CANONICAL FORM

$\mathbf{T} \leftarrow$ CLS-4 ($\mathbf{D}$, k)

PROGRAM

Main program, Program 13.

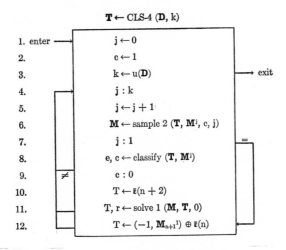

PROGRAM 13. CLS-4 main routine.

CLS-5 DESCRIPTION

This system differs from CLS-1 only in the specification of a sample. (In this it is similar to CLS-4.) The sample is determined using the *sample 3* program instead of *sample 1*. This causes a change in the main routine only. The solution routine is *solv 1*.

CANONICAL FORM

$$\mathbf{T} \leftarrow \text{CLS-5} (\mathbf{D}, k)$$

PROGRAM

Main routine, Program 14.

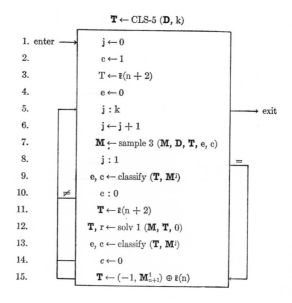

PROGRAM 14. Main routine of CLS-5.

CLS-6 DESCRIPTION

This system is identical to CLS-1 except that subproblems are selected, within the solution routine, by using the subtraction criterion (and, hence, the *subslct* program) instead of the maximum frequency criterion.

CANONICAL FORM

$\mathbf{T} \leftarrow$ CLS-6 $(\mathbf{D}, k)$

PROGRAM

Solution routine identical to Program 12 (*solv 1*) except that *subslct* replaces all references to *maxslct*, and a new solution routine, *solv 2*, is thus defined.

Main routine is identical to Program 11 (*CLS-1*) except that *solv 2* replaces all references to *solv 1*, thus defining *CLS-6*.

CLS-7 Description

The system is identical to CLS-1 except that a new solution routine, *solv 3*, is substituted for *solv 1*. In *solv 3* the "positive instances" are defined, at each node, as the largest of the two sets; experimenter designated positive instances and experimenter designated negative instances. The *maxslct* program is used after this definition is made.

Canonical Form

$\mathbf{T} \leftarrow CLS\text{-}7\ (\mathbf{D},\ \mathrm{k})$

Program

Main routine is identical to CLS-1 main routine (Program 11) except that reference to *solv 3* replaces all reference to *solv 1*.

Solution routine, Program 15.

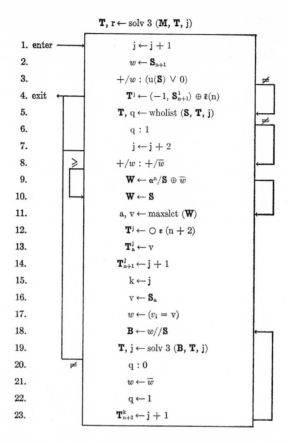

$$\mathbf{T}, r \leftarrow \text{solv } 3 \ (\mathbf{M}, \mathbf{T}, j)$$

1. enter	$j \leftarrow j + 1$	
2.	$w \leftarrow \mathbf{S}_{n+1}$	
3.	$+/w : (u(\mathbf{S}) \lor 0)$	$\neq$
4. exit	$\mathbf{T}^j \leftarrow (-1, \mathbf{S}^1_{n+1}) \oplus \mathbf{\check{e}}(n)$	
5.	$\mathbf{T}, q \leftarrow \text{wholist } (\mathbf{S}, \mathbf{T}, j)$	$\neq$
6.	$q : 1$	
7.	$j \leftarrow j + 2$	
8.	$+/w : +/\overline{w}$	
9.	$\mathbf{W} \leftarrow \alpha^n/\mathbf{S} \oplus \overline{w}$	
10.	$\mathbf{W} \leftarrow \mathbf{S}$	
11.	$a, v \leftarrow \text{maxslct } (\mathbf{W})$	
12.	$\mathbf{T}^j \leftarrow \bigcirc \ \mathbf{e} \ (n + 2)$	
13.	$\mathbf{T}^j_a \leftarrow v$	
14.	$\mathbf{T}^j_{n+1} \leftarrow j + 1$	
15.	$k \leftarrow j$	
16.	$v \leftarrow \mathbf{S}_a$	
17.	$w \leftarrow (v_i = v)$	
18.	$\mathbf{B} \leftarrow w//\mathbf{S}$	
19.	$\mathbf{T}, j \leftarrow \text{solv } 3 \ (\mathbf{B}, \mathbf{T}, j)$	
20.	$q : 0$	
21.	$w \leftarrow \overline{w}$	
22.	$q \leftarrow 1$	
23.	$\mathbf{T}^k_{n+2} \leftarrow j + 1$	

PROGRAM 15. Definition of solv 3 routine. Routine solv 4 is defined identically except that the inequality in line 8 is replaced, and *solv 4* replaces *solv 3* in the recursive reentry at line 19.

CLS-8 DESCRIPTION

This system is identical to CLS-7 except that the smaller, rather than the larger, of the two experimenter defined classes is used as the class of positive instances.

CANONICAL FORM

T ← CLS-8 (**D**, k)

PROGRAMS

Main routine, Program 11 (CLS-1 main routine) except that all references to *solv 1* are replaced by references to *solv 4*.

Solution routine. A new program, *solv 4*, is defined to be identical to *solv 3*, Program 15, except that "≤" replaces "≥" in line 8 of Program 15.

Summaries of Statistical Tests, Experiments IV, V, and VI

1. EXPERIMENT IV

UNTRANSFORMED SCORES—ERRORS

Source	D.f.	mS
1. Program type	1	7.701
2. Sequence of Stimuli	4	101.851
3. Memory size	2	449.705
4. Problem types	4	6216.737
5. $(1) \times (2)$	4	9.985
6. $(1) \times (3)$	2	1.697
7. $(1) \times (4)$	4	3.752
8. $(2) \times (3)$	8	32.035
9. $(2) \times (4)$	16	111.231
10. $(3) \times (4)$	8	39.237
11. $(1) \times (2) \times (3)$	8	11.231
12. $(1) \times (2) \times (4)$	16	18.864
13. $(1) \times (3) \times (4)$	8	6.842
14. $(2) \times (3) \times (4)$	32	13.842
15. $(1) \times (2) \times (3) \times (4)$	32	10.778
16. Replications	600	5.317

LOG TRANSFORMED SCORES—ERRORS

Source	D.f.	mS $(\times 10^3)$
1. Program type	1	5.24
2. Sequence of stimui	4	351.15
3. Memory size	2	10.66
4. Problem types	4	45555.51
5. $(1) \times (2)$	4	246.44
6. $(1) \times (3)$	2	75.28
7. $(1) \times (4)$	4	14.97
8. $(2) \times (3)$	8	85.69
9. $(2) \times (4)$	16	321.12
10. $(3) \times (4)$	8	213.78
11. $(1) \times (2) \times (3)$	8	126.76
12. $(1) \times (2) \times (4)$	16	384.43
13. $(1) \times (3) \times (4)$	8	225.09
14. $(2) \times (3) \times (4)$	32	197.15
15. $(1) \times (2) \times (3) \times (4)$	32	202.70
16. Replications	600	31.09

UNTRANSFORMED SCORES—COMPUTATION CYCLES

Source	D.f.	mS ($\times 10^{-3}$)
1. Program type	1	193.218
2. Sequence	4	87535.367
3. Memory	2	40485.243
4. Problem type	4	1159396.676
5. (1) $\times$ (2)	4	38267.784
6. (1) $\times$ (3)	2	32898.436
7. (1) $\times$ (4)	4	175.616
8. (2) $\times$ (3)	8	16301.028
9. (2) $\times$ (4)	16	128472.784
10. (3) $\times$ (4)	8	63780.544
11. (1) $\times$ (2) $\times$ (3)	8	5216.234
12. (1) $\times$ (2) $\times$ (4)	16	58888.656
13. (1) $\times$ (3) $\times$ (4)	8	43874.272
14. (2) $\times$ (3) $\times$ (4)	32	36188.544
15. (1) $\times$ (2) $\times$ (3) $\times$ (4)	32	33835.568
16. Replications	600	5672.819

UNTRANSFORMED SCORES—EXTRAPOLATED ERRORS

Source	D.f.	mS
1. Program type	1	22.881
2. Sequence	4	1681.549
3. Memory	2	15736.963
4. Problem type	4	152870.621
5. (1) $\times$ (2)	4	1573.891
6. (1) $\times$ (3)	2	177.383
7. (1) $\times$ (4)	4	2594.404
8. (2) $\times$ (3)	8	1862.172
9. (2) $\times$ (4)	16	1644.109
10. (3) $\times$ (4)	8	2952.566
11. (1) $\times$ (2) $\times$ (3)	8	243.971
12. (1) $\times$ (2) $\times$ (4)	16	610.109
13. (1) $\times$ (3) $\times$ (4)	8	365.689
14. (2) $\times$ (3) $\times$ (4)	32	1066.854
15. (1) $\times$ (2) $\times$ (3) $\times$ (4)	32	374.721
16. Replications	600	377.218

2. EXPERIMENT V

ERRORS

Source	D.f.	mS ($\times 10^3$)	F
1. Problem type	3	76.28	52.29
2. Memory size	2	20.57	14.10
3. Program type	1	2.91	1.99
4. (1) $\times$ (2)	6	5.07	3.48
5. (1) $\times$ (3)	3	1.31	1.12
6. (2) $\times$ (3)	2	1.27	1.15
7. (1) $\times$ (2) $\times$ (3)	6	2.28	1.16
8. Remainder	96	1.46	

COMPUTATION CYCLES

Source	D.f.	mS ($\times 10^3$)	F
1. Problem	3	631.488	51.51
2. Memory	2	5.124	>1
3. Program	1	15.509	1.27
4. (1) $\times$ (2)	6	22.081	1.80
5. (1) $\times$ (3)	3	11.312	>1
6. (2) $\times$ (3)	2	45.824	3.74
7. (1) $\times$ (2) $\times$ (3)	6	6.155	>1
8. Remainder	96	12.259	

ACCURACY (CG) SCORES

Source	D.f.	mS ($\times 10^3$)	F
1. Problem	3	7.429	31.68
2. Memory	2	1.286	5.48
3. Program	1	2.047	8.73
4. (1) $\times$ (2)	6	.354	1.51
5. (1) $\times$ (3)	3	1.201	5.12
6. (2) $\times$ (3)	2	.278	1.19
7. (1) $\times$ (2) $\times$ (3)	6	.301	1.28
8. Remainder	96	.235	

Log Transformed Error Scores

Source	D.f.	mS ($\times 10^3$)	F
1. Problems	3	76.282	52.29
2. Memory size	2	20.574	14.10
3. Programs	1	2.906	1.99
4. (1) $\times$ (2)	6	5.072	3.48
5. (1) $\times$ (3)	3	1.307	<1
6. (2) $\times$ (3)	2	1.271	<1
7. (1) $\times$ (2) $\times$ (3)	6	2.275	1.56
8. Replications	96	1.459	

Log Transformed Computation Cycle Score

Source	D.f.	mS ($\times 10^3$)	F
1. Problems	3	631.488	51.51
2. Memory size	2	5.124	2.39
3. Programs	1	15.509	1.27
4. (1) $\times$ (2)	6	22.081	1.80
5. (1) $\times$ (3)	3	11.312	<1
6. (2) $\times$ (3)	2	45.824	3.74
7. (1) $\times$ (2) $\times$ (3)	6	6.155	<1
8. Replications	96	12.259	

Log Transformed CG Scores

Source	D.f.	mS ($\times 10^3$)	F
1. Problems	3	7.429	31.68
2. Memory size	2	1.286	5.48
3. Programs	1	2.047	8.73
4. (1) $\times$ (2)	6	.354	1.51
5. (1) $\times$ (3)	3	1.201	5.12
6. (2) $\times$ (3)	2	.278	1.19
7. (1) $\times$ (2) $\times$ (3)	6	.301	1.28
8. Replications	96	.235	

3. EXPERIMENT VI

Log Transformed Error Scores

Source	D.f.	mS ($\times 10^3$)	F
1. Problems	3	82.627	75.05
2. Memory size	2	.346	>1
3. Programs	1	4.273	3.88
4. (1) × (2)	6	.505	>1
5. (1) × (3)	3	.900	>1
6. (2) × (3)	2	1.592	1.45
7. (1) × (2) × (3)	6	.734	>1
8. Replications	96	1.101	

Log Transformed Computation Cycle Scores

Source	D.f.	mS ($\times 10^3$)	F
1. Problems	3	644.802	64.60
2. Memory size	2	1.992	>1
3. Programs	1	.663	>1
4. (1) × (2)	6	6.068	>1
5. (1) × (3)	3	3.176	>1
6. (2) × (3)	2	5.728	>1
7. (1) × (2) × (3)	6	4.323	>1
8. Replications	96	9.982	

Log Transformed CG Scores

Source	D.f.	mS ($\times 10^3$)	F
1. Problems	3	.397	2.71
2. Memory size	2	.274	1.87
3. Programs	1	.668	4.57
4. (1) × (2)	6	.183	1.25
5. (1) × (3)	3	.305	2.09
6. (2) × (3)	2	.274	1.87
7. (1) × (2) × (3)	6	.168	1.15
8. Replications	96	**.146**	

An Algol Program Defining CLS-9

1. INTRODUCTION

This appendix contains an Algol program for defining and conducting the experiments reported in Chapter 5 for CLS-9. This program has been run using the English Electric KIDSGROVE and WHETSTONE Algol compilers. The only difference between these compilers, insofar as a user is concerned, is that the former is a fast execute, slow compile system while the latter is the reverse (Randell and Russell, 1964). Linguistically, they are nearly identical. The only major way in which either differ from a complete Algol system, as defined in the revised Algol report (Naur *et al.*, 1962), is that they forbid dynamic own arrays.

This restriction is, in fact, important in writing a concept learning system. The current decision tree of the CLS is stored as a two-dimensional array, using Iverson's right tree notation. It is necessary to define the estimated maximum size of this array before beginning a particular concept learning problem. This is done by specifying a parameter in a block containing the main working block, in which the problem solving computations are done. The program then enters the working block and carries out the necessary computations. These include reading (pseudo reading, by internal generation of data) new instances as they occur. If it becomes evident that insufficient space has been allotted for the decision tree, the program exits from the working block to a special location in the outer block. At this point the parameter establishing the size of the array for holding the tree is increased. The problem is then begun anew. This is necessary since the program cannot return to its position in the original problem because all intermediate calculations were lost when the inner (working) block was left to report that more space was needed. This problem could have been avoided by defining the CLS-9 memory array as an own array belonging to the outer block, which unfortunately was not done. The alternative, and more straightforward method, would have been to define the array holding the tree as a dynamic own array global to the inner block. This was not permitted by the compiler.

To aid in reading the program, the following points should be noted.

(a) All procedures are listed immediately after the declarations of the outermost block, and thus are global to the entire program. The procedures include a random number generator and a categorization routine which, in essence, conducts the experiments specified by Problem Set I. The heart of the CLS program is in the procedure "newtree," which defines the current decision rule.

(b) The parameters of the experimental situation are established in the two outermost blocks. The actual workings of the experiment and the CLS-9 algorithm are contained in the "main working block."

(c) The memory system is, in fact, a systematic rather than a random procedure. Since the data used were generated randomly, this does not introduce any bias in the amount of information available to the problem solving section of the program.

(d) Since the appendix was set from the computer program, two deviations from publication Algol should be noted. Reserved symbols are underlined instead of being set in boldface. The KDF-9 input-output functions are included. Their action should be clear from context.

2. PROGRAM   (begins on page 231)

```
begin
comment  Program for one problem binary concept study;

integer  coin, attrib, value, f1, f2, f3, report, i, temp, sample, error,
memory, problem, junk, repeats, maxht;
boolean  result, restart;

comment  Procedures needed;

library  A0, A6;

real procedure  random (a, b, x0);
value  a, b, x0; real  a, b; integer  x0;
begin
      own integer  m35, m36, m37, x;
      if x0 ≠ 0 then
      begin
            x: = x0;
            m35: = 34  359  738  368;
            m36: = 68  719  476  736;
            m37: = 137  438  953  472;
      end;
      x: = 5 × x;
      if × ≥ m37 then x: = x - m37;
      if × ≥ m36 then x: = x - m36;
      if × ≥ m35 then x: = x - m35;
      random: = x/m35 × (b - a) + a;
end;

procedure  newtree (tree, maxht, data, n, k, b, c, result);
value  maxht, k, b, c, n;
integer array  tree, data;
integer  maxht, n, k, b, c; boolean  result;

comment  Produces a decision tree of depth maxht or less from data array of
n cases with k attributes and b values, divided into c classes;

begin
      integer  node, i, j, temp, y;

comment  Initialize at entry;
      for i: = 1 step 1 until maxht do
      tree [i, 1]: = tree [i, 2]: = 0;
      for i: = 1 step 1 until n do
      data [i, 0]: = 1; y: = 2;

      comment  Iterate over each node;

      for node : = 1 step 1 until maxht do
      begin
            comment  Test to see if finished;
            if node = y then goto thru;
            comment  Search data;
            for j : = 1 step 1 until n do
            if data [j, 0] = node then goto active;
      comment  Passage indicates no active data;
```

```
L:     end Frequencies established;
       comment Begin section to select test;

       if prob then goto node;

       comment Passage here indicates problem does not exist;

       tree [x, 2] : = 0; goto out;

       comment Passage here for an interior node of tree;

node: max : = 0.0; tree [x, 2] : = y;
      hold : = 0;
      for i : = 1 step 1 until d do
      begin
              if check [i] > hold then
              begin
                     hold : = check [i];
                     q : = i;
              end;
      end;
      for i : = 1 step 1 until b do
      begin
              temp : = 0.0;
              for j : = 0 step 1 until c - 1 do
              begin
                      cmax : = 0.0;
                      for k : = 1 step 1 until d do
                      if freq [ i, j, k] > cmax then cmax : = freq [i, j, k];
                      temp : = temp + cmax;
              end;
              if temp ≤ max then goto next;
              max : = temp; tree [x, 1] : = i;
next: end Line has been set up;
      if max ≤ hold then
      begin
              tree [x, 1] : = q; tree [x, 2] : = 0;
              writetext (30, [[c] no*local*optimizer[c]] );
              writetext (30, [frequencies*are] );
              for k : = 1 step 1 until d do
              write (30, format ([nddss]), check [k] );
              writetext (30, [[c]] );
      end;
out : end Select procedure;

integer procedure classify (item, tree);
integer array item, tree;

comment Finds classification of item in tree;

begin
        integer i;
        i : = 1;
test: if tree [i, 2] = 0 then goto leaf;
      i : = tree [i, 2] + item [tree [i, 1]];
      goto test;
```

```
             goto nextnode;
active:      select (tree, node, y, data, n, k, b, c, j);
             if tree [node, 2] = 0 then goto nextnode;

             comment Adjustment at interior node;

             temp: = tree [node, 1];
             for i: = j step 1 until n do
             begin
                   if data[i,0] ≠ node then goto again;
                   data [i,0]: = y + data [i, temp];
again:       end;
                   y: = y + b; if y > maxht then goto oversize;
nextnode : end;

         comment Passage here indicates tree OK;

thru: result: = true; goto out;
oversize:result: = false;
     writetext (30, [size*failure[c]]);
out:end procedure newtree;

procedure select (tree, x, y, data, a, b, c, d, e);
value x, y, a, b, c, d, e; integer array tree, data; integer x, y, a, b, c, d, e;
comment This is the selection function for CLS-9. It selects node x of a tree
with successor y in right tree order. Data has a cases, b attributes, c values
per attribute (a slight specialization), d classes, and the first active data is
case e;

begin
     comment Find frequency table;

     array freq [1:b, 0:c-1, 1:d]; integer array check [1:d];
     integer i, j, k, s, hold, q; boolean prob;
     real max, cmax, temp;

     comment First zero table;

     for i: = 1 step 1 until b do
     for j: = 0 step 1 until c-1 do
     for k: = 1 step 1 until d do freq [i, j, k]: = 0. 0;
     prob: = false;
     tree [x,1]: = data [e, b + 1];
     for k: = 1 step 1 until d do check [k]: = 0 ;

     comment Begin frequency count;

     for s: = e step 1 until a do
     begin
             goto if data [s,0] ≠ x then L
             else if prob or (data [s, b + 1] = tree [x, 1]) then count else mark;
mark:        prob: = true;
count:       for i: = 1 step 1 until b do
             freq [i, data[s,i], data [s,b + 1]]: = freq[i, data[s,i],
             data[s, b + 1]] + 1. 0;
             k: = data [s, b + 1];
             check [k]: = check [k] + 1 ;
```

```
leaf:  if tree [i, 1] = 0 then
           writetext (30, [adjustment [c]]);
           classify : = tree [i, 1];
end classification procedure;
integer procedure category (item, j);
integer array item; integer j;

comment Finds true class in problem set 1;

begin
        switch  sw : = s1, s2, s3, s4, s4;
        boolean test trial;
        test : = (j ≠ 5); goto sw [j];
s1:    trial : = item [1] = 0 and item [2] = 0; goto out;
s2:    trial : = item [1] = 0 or item [2] = 0; goto out;
s3:    trial : = item [1] = 0 imp item [2] = 0; goto out;
s4:    trial : = item [1] = 0 eqv item [2] = 0; goto out;
out:  if test then goto quit; trial : = not trial;

quit: category : = if trial then 1 else 2;
end categorization procedure;


comment Output setup;
f1 : = format ([nddc]); f2 : = format ([nddss]); f3 : = format ([nddddddddddcc]);

comment Start driver for simple study by reading parameters;

open (20); open (30); coin: = read (20); report: = read (20);
junk: = random (0, 1, coin);

comment Random number and report generator set up;

attrib: = read (20); value: = read (20); sample: = read (20); repeats: = read (20);
problem: = read (20); memory: = read (20); maxht: = read (20);

comment Report type of experiment;

writetext (30, [concept*learning*study]);
writetext (30, [[c]problem*structure[s]]);
writetext (30, [attributes [2s]]); write (30, f2, attrib);
writetext (30, [values*per*attribute]); write (30, f1, value);
writetext (30, [Problem*type[2s]]); write (30, f2, problem);
writetext (30, [Repetitions [2s]]); write (30, f1, repeats);
writetext (30, [initial*value*of*random*number [2s]]); write (30, f3, coin);
writetext (30, [data*for*each*run [2s]]);
writetext (30, [sample*size**]); write (30, f2, sample);
writetext (30, [memory*size*]); write (30, f2, memory);
writetext (30, [tree*size**]); write (30, f1, maxht);

restart: = false;

comment Find frequency of types;

begin
        integer array freq [1:attrib, 0:value], data [1:memory, 0:attrib + 1];
        integer j, k, l, q;
```

<u>comment</u> Main working block;

<u>for</u> i: = 1 <u>step</u> 1 <u>until</u> attrib <u>do</u>
     <u>begin</u>
         <u>comment</u> Find frequencies;

         temp: = 0; writetext (30, [[3c]]);
         writetext (30, [relative*frequencies*for*attribute**]); write
         (30, f1, i);
         <u>for</u> j: = 1 <u>step</u> 1 <u>until</u> value <u>do</u>
         <u>begin</u>
             freq [i, j]: = read (20);
             temp: = temp + freq [i, j];
             write (30, f1, freq [i, j]);
         <u>end</u>
         freq [i, 0]: = temp;
     <u>end</u> Frequencies found;

     <u>comment</u> Now start action at each repetition;

     <u>if</u> report = 1 <u>then</u> writetext (30, [full*report]) <u>else</u> writetext (30,
     [summary*report]);
     writetext (30, [[ccc]]);
go: <u>begin</u>
         <u>comment</u> Define tree;
         <u>integer array</u> tree [1: maxht, 1:2];
         <u>for</u> i: = 1 <u>step</u> 1 <u>until</u> repeats <u>do</u>
         <u>begin</u>
             <u>comment</u> Action at repetition;
             <u>integer</u> errors;
             writetext (30, [[p]]); errors: = 0;
             writetext (30, [repetition**]); write (30, f1, i);

             <u>comment</u> Clean tree and data;

             <u>for</u> j: = 1 <u>step</u> 1 <u>until</u> maxht <u>do</u> tree [j, 1]: = tree [j, 2]: = 0;
             <u>for</u> j: = 1 <u>step</u> 1 <u>until</u> memory <u>do</u>
             <u>begin</u>
                 data [j, 0]: = 1;
                 <u>for</u> k: = 1 <u>step</u> 1 <u>until</u> attrib + 1 <u>do</u> data [j, k]: = 0;
             <u>end</u>;
             error: = 0;

             <u>comment</u> Action at each item follows;

             <u>for</u> 1: = 1 <u>step</u> 1 <u>until</u> sample <u>do</u>
             <u>begin</u>
                 <u>comment</u> Block for one item;

                 <u>integer array</u> item [1: attrib + 1];

                 <u>comment</u> Get values for item;

                 <u>for</u> j: = 1 <u>step</u> 1 <u>until</u> attrib <u>do</u>
                 <u>begin</u>
                    <u>comment</u> Assign value j;

```
                              junk: = 0; temp: = random (0, freq [j, 0], 0);
                              for k: = 1 step 1 until value do
                              begin
                                    junk: = junk + freq [j, k];
                                    if junk ≥ temp then goto assign;

                              end;
assign:                       item [j]: = k - 1;
                              end Item defined;
                              item [attrib + 1]: = category (item, problem);
                              if report = 1 then
                              begin
                                    for j: = 1 step 1 until attrib do
                                    write (30, f2, item [j]) ;
                                    write (30, f1, item [attrib + 1]);
                              end;

                              comment Store item;

                              q: = if memory ≥ 1 then 1 else 1 - memory × (1÷ memory);
                              for j: = 1 step 1 until attrib + 1 do data [q, j]: = item [ j ];
                              goto if 1 = 1 then guess else if item [attrib + 1] ≠
                              classify (item, tree)
                              then goof else onward;
goof:                         error: = error + 1;
                              goto if report = 1 then record else guess;
record:                       writetext (30, [error*]) ; write (30, f1, error);
guess:                        newtree (tree, maxht, data, (if 1 < memory then 1 else
                              memory),
                              attrib, value, 2, result);
                              goto if result then run else walk;
run:                          if report = 1 then goto rec 2 else goto cleanup;
rec 2:                        writetext (30, [tree*is [2c]]);
                              for j : = 1 step 1 until maxht do
                              begin
                                    if tree [j, 1] = 0 and tree [j, 2] = 0 then goto around;
                                    write (30, f2, j);
                                    write (30, f2, tree [j, 1]);
                                    write (30, f1, tree [j, 2]);
around:                       end Reporting finished;
                              writetext (30, [memory [c]]);
                              writetext (30, [memory [c]]);
                              for j: = 1 step 1 until memory do
                              begin
                                    for q: = 1 step 1 until attrib do
                                    write (30, f2, data [j, q]);
                                    write (30, f1, data [j, attrib + 1]);
                              end:
                              writetext (30, [[2c]]);
cleanup:                      for j: = 1 step 1 until memory do data [j, 0]: = 1;
onward:              end routine for each item;

                     comment Block finished;

                     writetext (30, [[cc] total*errors]);
                     write (30, f1, error);
```

```
                    error: = 0;
                    writetext (30, [[c] Final*tree [c]]) ;
                    for j: = 1 step 1 until maxht do
                    begin
                            if tree [j, 1] + tree [j, 2] = 0 then goto still;
                            write (30, f2, j);
                            write (30, f2, tree [j, 1]);
                            write (30, f1, tree [j, 2]);
  still:                end;
                end computations for one repetition;
          end;

          comment All repetitions thru;
  walk: if result then goto finale;

          comment Readjust parameters and store;

          writetext (30, [tree*size*adjusted*to**]) ;
          maxht: = maxht + 50; repeats: = repeats + 1 - i;
          write (30, f1, maxht); restart: = true; goto go;
  end main working block;
  finale:close(20); close (30);
  end →
```

REFERENCES

Abelson, R. P., and Tukey, J. W., 1959. Efficient conversion of non-metric into metric information. *Proc. Am. Statistical Assoc., Social Statistics Sect.* pp. 226–230.

Anderson, T., 1958. "An Introduction to Multivariate Statistical Analysis." Wiley, New York.

Anscombe, F. J. 1964. Some remarks on Bayesian statistics, *in* "Human Judgements and Optimality" (M. W. Shelly and G. L. Bryan, eds.), Wiley, New York.

Atkinson, R., and Estes, W., 1963. Stimulus sampling theory, *in* "Handbook of Mathematical Psychology" (R. D. Luce, R. Bush, and E. Galanter, eds.), Vol. 2, p. 121. Wiley, New York.

Attneave, F., 1959. "Applications of Information Theory to Psychology." Holt, New York.

Banerji, R., 1962. The description list of concepts. *Comm. Assoc. Computing Machinery* **5,** 426–431.

Bartlett, F., 1958. "Thinking." Basic Books, New York.

Berelson, B., 1954. Content analysis, *in* "Handbook of Social Psychology" (R. Lindzey, ed.), p. 488. Addison-Wesley, Reading, Massachusetts.

Bower, G., and Trabasso, T. 1963a. Concept identification, *in* "Studies in Mathematical Psychology" (R. Atkinson, ed.), p. 32. Stanford Univ. Press, Stanford, California.

Bower, G., and Trabasso, T., 1963b. Reversals prior to solution in concept learning. *J. Exptl. Psychol.* **66,** 409–418.

Braley, L. 1962. Paper presented at Western Psych. Assoc. Meetings, San Francisco, California.

Bruner, J. S., Goodnow, J. J., and Austin, G. A., 1956. "A Study of Thinking." Wiley, New York.

Church, A. A., 1958. "Introduction to Mathematical Logic." Princeton Univ. Press, Princeton, New Jersey.

Crawford, J., Hunt, E. B., and Peak, G., 1965. One trial learning and improvement with practice in disjunctive concept learning. Basser Computing Dept., Univ. of Sydney, Report, 1965.

Dobzhansky, T., 1962. "Mankind Evolving." Yale Univ. Press, New Haven, Connecticut.

Edwards, W., Lindman, T., and Savage, R., 1963. Bayesian statistical inference for psychological research. *Psychol. Rev.* **70,** 193–242.

Estes, W. K., 1964. All or none processes in learning and retention. *Am. Psychologist* **19,** 16–25.

Feigenbaum, E. A., 1961. The simulation of verbal learning behavior. *Proc. Western Joint Computer Conf.* **1961** pp. 121–132.

Feigenbaum, E. A., and Simon, H. A., 1963. Performance of a reading task by an elementary perceiving and memorizing program. *Behavioral Sci.* **8,** 72–76.

Feldman, J., 1962. Computer simulation of cognitive processes, *in* "Computer Applications in the Behavioral Sciences" (H. Borko, ed.), p. 336. Prentice-Hall, Englewood Cliffs, New Jersey.

Fischler, M., Mattson, R. L., Firschein, O., and Healy, L. D., 1962. An approach to general pattern recognition. *IRE (Inst. Radio Engrs.), Trans. Inform. Theory* **8,** 58–63.

Garner, W., 1962. "Information and Structure as Psychological Concepts." Wiley, New York.

Gillespie, J., and Allport, G. W., 1955. "Youth's Outlook on the Future." Doubleday, New York.

Green, B. F., Jr., 1963. "Computers in Research." McGraw-Hill, New York.

Harmon, H., 1960. "Modern Factor Analysis." Univ. of Chicago Press, Chicago, Illinois.

Haygood, R., and Bourne, L. E., 1965. Attribute and rule learning aspects of conceptual behavior. *Psychol. Rev.* **72,** 175–195.

Hovland, C. I., 1952. A "Communication Analysis" of concept learning. *Psychol. Rev.* **59,** 461–472.

Hunt, E. B., 1962. "Concept Learning: An Information Processing Problem." Wiley, New York.

Hunt, E. B., 1963. Simulation and analytic models of memory. *J. Verbal Learning Verbal Behavior* **2,** 49–59.

Hunt, E. B., 1964a. The evaluation of somewhat parallel models, *in* "Mathematical Explorations in Behavioral Sciences" (F. Massarik and P. Ratoosh, eds.), p. 37. Irwin, Homewood, Illinois, 1965.

Hunt, E. B., 1964b. Criteria for establishing locally optimal diagnostic test sequences. Basser Computing Dept., Univ. of Sydney, Technical Report.

Hunt, E. B., 1965. Selection and reception conditions in grammar and concept learning. *J. Verbal Learning Verbal Behavior* **4,** 211–215.

Hunt, E. B., and Hovland, C. I., 1960. Order of consideration of different types of concepts. *J. Exptl. Psychol.* **59,** 220–225.

Hunt, E. B., and Hovland, C. I., 1961. Programming a model of human concept formulation. *Proc. Western Joint Computer Conf., 1961* pp. 145–155.

Huxtable, D. R. H., 1964. On writing an optimizing translator for ALGOL 60, *in* "Introduction to System Programming" (P. Wegner, ed.), Chapter 9, p. 137. Academic Press, New York, 1964.

Iverson, K. E., 1962. "A Programming Language." Wiley, New York.

Iverson, K. E., 1964. Formalism in programming languages. *Comm. Assoc. Computing Machinery* **7,** 80–88.

Kepros, P., and Bourne, L., 1963. Paper read before Am. Psych. Assoc.

Kochen, M., 1961a. Experimental study of 'hypothesis-formation' by computer, *in* "Information Theory. 4th London Symposium" (C. Cherry, ed.). Butterworth, London and Washington, D.C.

Kochen, M., 1961b. An experimental program for the selection of "disjunctive hypotheses." *Proc. Western Joint Computer Conf., 1961* pp. 571–578.

Lewis, L., and Langford, H., 1932. "Symbolic Logic." Dover, New York.

Luce, R. D., ed., 1960. "Developments in Mathematical Psychology." Free Press, Glencoe, Illinois.

Luce, R. D., and Raiffa, H., 1957. "Games and Decisions." Wiley, New York.

McGeoch, J., and Irion, K., 1952. "The Psychology of Human Learning." Longmans, Green, New York.

Mattson, R. L., and Firschein, O., 1963. Feature word construction for use with pattern recognition algorithms: An experimental study. Lockheed Missiles and Space Company, Sunnyvale, California, Rept. No. 6-90-62-58.

Mattson, R. L., Firschein, O., and Fischler, M., 1963. An experimental investigation of a class of pattern recognition synthesis algorithms. *IEEE (Inst. Elec. Electron. Engrs.), Trans. Electron. Computers* **12,** 300–306.

Miller, G. A., 1956. The magical number seven, plus or minus two: Some limits on our capacity to process information. *Psychol. Rev.* **63**, 81–97.

Minsky, M., 1961. Steps toward artificial intelligence. *Proc. IRE* **49**, 8–30.

Naur, P., ed., 1960. Report on the Algorithmic Language ALGOL 60. *Comm. A.C.M.* **3**, No. 5, 314.

Naur, P., ed., 1962. Revised report on the Algorithmic Language ALGOL 60. *Comm. A.C.M.* **6**, 1–17.

Neisser, U., 1963. The imitation of man by machine. *Science* **139**, 193–197.

Neisser, U., and Weene, P., 1962. Hierarchies in concept attainment. *J. Exptl. Psychol.* **64**, 640–645.

Newell, A., ed., 1961. "Information Processing Language-V. Manual." Prentice-Hall, Englewood Cliffs, New Jersey.

Newell, A., ed., 1964. "Information Processing Language-V. Manual," 2nd ed. Prentice-Hall, Englewood Cliffs, New Jersey.

Newell, A., and Simon, H. A., 1961a. GPS, a program that simulates human thought, *in* "Lernende Automaten" (H. Billing, ed.), p. 109. Oldenbourg KG, Munich.

Newell, A., and Simon, H. A., 1961b. Computer simulation of human thinking. *Science* **134**, 2011–2017.

Newell, A., Shaw, J. C., and Simon, H. A., 1955. Current developments in complex information processing. *Rand Corp. Tech. Rept.*

Newell, A., Shaw, J., and Simon, H. A., 1957. Empirical explorations of the logic theory machine: a case study in heuristics. *Proc. Western Joint Computer Conf., 1957* 218–239.

Newell, A., Shaw, J. C., and Simon, H. A., 1958. Elements of a theory of human problem solving. *Psychol. Rev.* **65**, 151–166.

Newell, A., Shaw, J. C., and Simon, H. A., 1959. A variety of intelligent learning in the general problem solver. *Rand. Corp. Tech. Rept.* p. 1742.

Ogilvie, D., 1964. Unpublished paper. Lab. Social Relations, Harvard Univ.

Ogilvie, D., Dunphy, D., Smith, C., Stone, P. J., Shneidman, E., and Farberow, N., 1962. Some characteristics of genuine vs. simulated suicide notes analyzed by a computer system called the General Inquirer. Lab. Social Relations, Harvard Univ.

Polya, G., 1954. "Mathematics and Plausible Reasoning," 2 vols. Princeton Univ. Press, Princeton, New Jersey.

Randell, B., and Russell, L. J., 1964. "ALGOL 60 Implementation." Academic Press, New York.

Rao, C. R., 1952. "Advanced Statistical Methods in Biometric Research." Wiley, New York.

Rapoport, A., 1960. "Fights Games and Debates." Univ. of Michigan Press, Ann Arbor, Michigan.

Reed, H. B., 1946. The learning and retention of concepts, IV. The influence of the complexity of the stimuli. *J. Exptl. Psychol.* **36**, 252–261.

Reitman, W. R., 1965. "Computers and Thought: An Information Processing Approach." Wiley, New York.

Restle, F., 1961. "Psychology of Judgment and Choice." Wiley, New York.

Rosenblatt, F., 1962. "Principles of Neurodynamics." Spartan Press, Washington, D.C.

Sebesteyen, G., 1962. "Decision Making Processes in Pattern Recognition." Macmillan, New York.

Selfridge, O., 1959. Pandemonium; a paradigm for learning. *Proc. Symp. Mechanization Thought Processes,* **1958** p. 511. H.M. Stationery Office, London.

Scheffe, H., 1959. "The Analysis of Variance." Wiley, New York.

Shepard, R. N., Hovland, C. I., and Jenkins, H. M., 1961. Learning and memorization of classifications. *Psychol. Monograph* **75**, 13 (Whole No. 517).

Shneidman, E., and Farberow, N. L., 1957. "Clues to Suicide." McGraw-Hill, New York.

Simon, H. A., and Feigenbaum, E. A., 1964. An information-processing theory of some effects of similarity, familiarization, and meaningfulness in verbal learning. *J. Verbal Learning Verbal Behavior* **3**, 385.

Smith, T., Jones, L., and Thomas, S., 1963. Effects upon verbal learning of stimulus similarity number of stimuli per response and concept formation. *J. Verbal Learning Verbal Behavior* **1**, 470–476.

Snedecor, G., 1956. "Statistical Methods," 5th ed. Univ. of Iowa Press, Ames, Iowa.

Stone, P. J., and Hunt, E. B., 1963. A computer approach to content analysis: students using the general inquirer system. *Proc. Spring Joint Computer Conf., 1963* AFIPS 23, pp. 241–256.

Stone, P. J., Bales, R. F., Namenwirth, J. Z., and Ogilvie, D. M., 1962. The general inquirer: a computer system for content analysis and retrieval based on the sentence as a unit of information. *Behavioral Sci.* **7**, 484–498.

Suppes, P., 1960. "Introduction to Logic." Van Nostrand, Princeton, New Jersey.

Sutcliffe, P. J., 1957. A general method of analysis of frequency data for multiple classification designs. *Psychol. Bull.* **54**, 134–137.

Turing, A. M., 1950. Computing machinery and intelligence. *Mind* **59**, 433–460.

Uhr, L., 1963. Pattern recognition computers as models for form perception. *Psychol. Bull.* **60**, 40–73.

Uhr, L., and Vossler, C., 1961. A pattern recognition program that generates, evaluates, and adjusts its own operators. *Proc. Western Joint Computer Conference 1961* pp. 555–569.

Uhr, L., and Vossler, C., 1963. A pattern recognition program that generates, evaluates, and adjusts its own operators, *in* "Computers and Thought" (E. A. Feigenbaum and J. Feldman, eds.), p. 251. McGraw-Hill, New York.

Uhr, L., Vossler, C., and Uleman, J., 1962. Pattern recognition over distortions, by human subjects and by a computer simulation of a model for human perception. *J. Exptl. Psychol.* **63**, 227–234.

Underwood, B. J., and Schulz, R. W., 1960. "Meaningfulness and Verbal Learning." Lippincott, Philadelphia, Pennsylvania.

von Neumann, J., and Morgenstern, O., 1948. "Theory of Games." Princeton Univ. Press, Princeton, New Jersey.

Wason, P. C., 1960. On the failure to eliminate hypotheses in a conceptual task. *Quart J. Exptl. Psychol.* **12**, 129–140.

Wason, P. C., 1961. Response to affirmative and negative binary statements. *Brit. J. Psychol.* **52**, 133–142.

Watanabe, S., 1960. Information theoretical aspects of inductive and deductive inference. *IBM J. Res. Develop.* **4**, 208–231.

Wells, H. H., 1963. The effects of transfer in disjunctive concept formation. *J. Exptl. Psychol.* **65**, 63–69.

Yngve, V., 1961. "COMIT Programmers Reference Manual." M.I.T. Press, Cambridge, Massachusetts.

AUTHOR INDEX

Numbers in italics refer to pages on which the complete references are listed.

A

Abelson, R. P., 105, *239*
Allport, G. W., 165, *240*
Anderson, T., 176, *239*
Anscombe, F. J., 115, *239*
Atkinson, R., 140, *239*
Attneave, F., 96, *239*
Austin, G. A., 12, 21, 22, 29, 33, 87, 114, 119, 133, *239*

B

Bales, R. F., 9, 153, 154, *242*
Banerji, R., 7, *239*
Bartlett, F., 147, *239*
Berelson, B., 151, *239*
Bourne, L., 120, 136, *240*
Bower, G., 135, 188, *239*
Braley, L., 136, *239*
Bruner, J. S., 12, 21, 22, 29, 33, 87, 114, 119, 133, *239*

C

Church, A. A., 10, *239*
Colby, B. M., *239*
Collier, G. A., *239*
Crawford, J., 189, *239*

D

Dobzhansky, T., 37, *239*
Dunphy, D., *241*

E

Edwards, W., 102, 115, *239*
Estes, W., 140, 188, *239*

F

Farberow, N., 164, *241*
Feigenbaum, E. A., 86, 190, 191, 192, *239*
Feldman, J., 119, 140, *239*
Firschein, O., 181, 183, *239, 240*
Fischler, M., 181, 183, *239, 240*

G

Garner, W., 60, 67, 95, 134, *240*
Gillespie, J., 165, *240*
Goodnow, J. J., 12, 21, 22, 29, 33, 87, 114, 119, 133, *239*
Green, B. F., Jr., 168, *240*

H

Harmon, H., 194, *240*
Haygood, R., 120, 136, *240*
Healy, L. D., 181, *239*
Hovland, C. I., 11, 46, 86, 128, 134, 135, 193, *240, 242*
Hunt, E. B., 7, 10, 11, 12, 29, 39, 46, 60, 84, 115, 116, 134, 136, 154, 171, 189, 191, *239, 240, 242*
Huxtable, D. R. H., 108, *240*

I

Irion, K., 190, *240*
Iverson, K., 5, 18, 108, 197, 199, *240*

J

Jenkins, H. M., 86, 128, 134, 193, *242*
Jones, L., 193, *242*

K

Kepros, P., 136, *240*
Kochen, M., 11, 12, 135, *240*

L

Langford, H., 37, *240*
Lewis, L., 37, *240*
Lindman, T., 102, 115, *239*
Luce, R. D., 95, 100, 102, *240*

M

McGeoch, J., 190, *240*
Mattson, R. L., 181, 183, *239, 240*
Miller, G. A., 191, *241*
Minsky, M., 4, 89, *241*
Morgenstern, O., 102, *242*

N

Namenwirth, J. Z., 9, 153, 154, *242*
Naur, P., 5, 107, 229, *241*
Neisser, U., 4, 134, *241*
Newell, A., 4, 5, 51, 119, *241*

O

Ogilvie, D., 9, 153, 154, *241, 242*

P

Peak, G., 189, *239*
Polya, G., 25, *241*
Postal, J. K., *239*

R

Raiffa, H., 100, 102, *240*
Randell, B., 6, 108, 229, *241*
Rao, C. R., 176, *241*
Rapoport, A., 102, *241*
Reed, H. B., 193, *241*
Reitman, W., 119, *241*
Restle, F., 7, *241*
Rosenblatt, F., 113, 179, *241*
Russell, L. J., 6, 108, 229, *241*

S

Savage, R., 102, 115, *239*
Scheffe, H., 54, 73, 125, 126, *241*
Schulz, R. W., 191, *242*
Sebesteyen, G., 10, 85, 175, *241*
Selfridge, O., 85, 179, *241*
Shaw, J., 4, 190, *241*
Shepard, R. N., 86, 128, 134, 193, *242*

Shneidman, E., 164, *241, 242*
Simon, H. A., 4, 119, 190, 191, 192, *239, 241*
Smith, C., *241*
Smith, T., 193, *242*
Snedecor, G., 54, 126, 142, 167, *242*
Stone, P. J., 9, 153, 154, *241, 242*
Suppes, P., 37, *242*
Sutcliffe, P. J., 167, *242*

T

Thomas, S., 193, *242*
Trabasso, T., 135, 188, *239*
Tukey, J. W., 105, *239*
Turing, A. M., 133, *242*

U

Uhr, L., 10, 85, 113, 186, 188, *242*
Uleman, J., 188, *242*
Underwood, B. J., 191, *242*

V

von Neumann, J., 102, *242*
Vossler, C., 113, 186, 188, *242*

W

Wason, P. C., 39, *242*
Watanabe, S., 68, 115, *242*
Weene, P., 134, *241*
Wells, H. H., 134, *242*

Y

Yngve, V., 159, *242*

SUBJECT INDEX

A

Adaptive techniques, 179
Algol, 5, 6, 107
Algorithm, 12
Artificial intelligence, 4, 6, 10, 34, 45, 67, 70, 84, 86, 87, 93, 113, 115, 135, 139, 152
Attribute, 7
  binary, 84
  relevant, 33, 65, 89
  irrelevant, 67
Attribute-value scheme, 8

B

Bartlett's test, 126
Bayesian induction, 68, 178, 193
  statistical procedures using, 102, 115
Biconditional, 37, 54, 56, 61, 98, 124, 127, 129, 131, 134, 136
Binary relation, 37

C

California money bill example, 159
Chance prediction, 143
Chi square, 95
Chunking, 191
Classification, 18, 21, 91, 109
  arbitrary, 139
  errors of, 33, 53, 60, 74, 78, 80, 81, 98, 113, 124, 128
CLS-1, 46, 71, 78, 79, 87, 90, 93, 114, 120, 123, 127, 129, 130, 131, 155
  -2, 71, 87, 110, 112, 188
  -3, 71, 87, 188
  -4, 88, 90
  -5, 88, 90, 114
  -6, 94, 97, 114
  -7, 97, 114, 129, 155
  -8, 97, 112, 114, 129, 155
  -9, 107, 112, 114, 129, 171, 188
Clustering, 179
COMIT, 159
Communication, 151
Compiler, 6, 229

Complexity of objects, 61, *see also* Attribute
Computation, 20
  amount of, 33, 72, 78, 81
  concept learning, *see* Concept learning
  cost of, 68, 75, 80
  evaluation, 32
Computation gain (CG), 73, 79, 81, 110
Computation time, 41, 54
Computer, 117
  model, 119
  program, 5, 100, 117
  simulation, 140
Concept, 10, 15, 114
  content of, 33
  form of, 126
  full form of, 15
  partial description of, 15
  partial form of, 15
  probabilistic, 153
  relational, 13
  structure of, 33
  tree form of, 19, 32, 33
Concept learning, 10, 25, 133
  errors during, 76
  human, 4, 22, 35, 46, 114, 119ff., 130
  problem defined, 32
  system defined, 3, 10
Condition of experiment, 51, 91
Conjunction, 12, 22, 37, 39, 40, 61, 64, 66, 76, 84, 93, 119, 124, 134, 136
Content of problem, 121, 126
Content analysis of text, 151, 168
Correlation, effect of spurious, 112
Cost factors in concept learning, 18, 69, 87, 99ff., 178

D

Decision making,
  criterion for, 99
  probabilistic, 11, 59
  rules for, 13, 89
  sequential, 16
  tree description of sequential, 17, 55, 94, 101, 107, 112

endpoint of, 17
incomplete, 112
leaf, 17
matrix representation, 18
node, 17
notation, 18ff.
root, 17
summary of, 162
Denotation, 10
Description,
of objects, 7, 14, 21, 32
space, 7, 41, 88
Diagnosis, medical, 4, 18
Diagnostic rules, 71
Dictionary in General Inquirer, 153
Dimension, *see* Attribute
Disjunction, 12, 98, 120, 134
exclusive, 37, 85, 124, 129, 130, 131, 134
inclusive, 37, 39, 40, 64, 112, 124
Disutility, 104
Document identification, 151

E

English Electric KDF 9 computer, 171
EPAM, 190ff.
Error rate, 52

F

Factor analysis, 194ff.
Feature word experiments, 180ff.
Filial-heir chain, 18
Focus, 22
Frequency, 93, 94, 112, 114
Future biographies example, 165ff.

G

Game against nature, 99ff.
Gene, 37
General Inquirer, the, 153ff.
Generalization, 67, 192
of results, 100

H

Hamming distance, 183
Hill climbing, 89
Hypothesis, 25, 76, 88

I

IBM 1401 computer, 159
IBM 7090 computer, 53, 123, 100

IBM 7094 computer, 159
Ignorance, complete, 103
Implication (logical connective), 37, 55, 61, 124
Individual differences, 137
Infection, bacterial, 101
Information, 72
multivariate, 134
probabilistic, 89
rate, 115
retrieval, 25, 31, 170
storage, 25, 115
transmitted, 95
Information Processing Language-V (IPL-V), 5, 51, 53, 97, 100, 107, 129, 159
Information theory, 116
Instances,
negative, 67, 72, 97, 127, 136, 140
positive, 66ff., 72, 93, 97, 114, 127ff., 136, 140
Iverson language, 6, 197ff.

L

Learning, *see also* Concept learning
all or none, 136, 188
human, 86, 115, 146
of logical connectives, 119ff.
paired associates, 190
device, 13
Legal driver, 16
Linear separability, 176
Linear weights, 179
List structure, 21
Liver disease example, 172
Local operators, 187
Logarithmic transformation, 74

M

Matrix, 19
Mean square distance, 176
Memory, 25, 31, 46, 55, 109, 112, 130
expandable, 31
fixed, 31
human, 25, 119
size of, 71ff., 171
Memory bank model, 11, 135
Minimax theorem, 102
Minimization, 18
Motor skills, 147

N

Name, 10
Negation, 38
New Guinea, *see* Liver disease example
Noise generator, 60
Nonsense syllables, 134, 140
Notation, 7, 14, 18
  for concept learning, 29
  Iverson, *see* Iverson language
Null element, 8

O

Object, 7, 10
Observation, 94, 115
  random, 87

P

Pandemonium pattern recognition
  scheme, 85, 179
Pattern recognition, 10, 85, 101, 113, 175,
  186
Perception, 113, 179
Perceptual units, 191
Predictability score, 143
Probability, 102
Problem, 72
  difficulty of, 123, 131
  redefinition of, 97
  Set I, 35, 54, 72, 80, 113, 118, 121
  Set II, 39, 64, 77, 90
  Set III, 64, 90
  structure of, 77, 116
Problem solving by humans, 4, 188,
    see also Learning, human
  time required, 128ff.
Project MAC, 159
Psychological experiments, 29, *see also*
  Concept learning
Psychology, 10, 141

R

Random categorization task, 139ff.
Recursive function, 48
Relevance, *see* Attribute, relevant
Response
  pattern, 146
  predicted, 131, 133, 142

Restricted interest, 34
Rule learning, 118

S

Sample, 10
  suboptimal, 88
  represented by matrix, 30
  size, 67
Selection, 25, 46, 66, 68, 91, 109, 114
  interactive, 31
  of subproblems, 93ff.
  random, 46, 61, 71
Selection procedure, 87, 90
Selection system, 26
Sequence, 87, 130
  information content of, 124, *see also*
    Observations, random
Sequential analysis, 165
Sequential word dependency, 182
Signal detection, 60
Simulation, 35, 129, 131, 140
  Monte Carlo, 116
Speech, 151
Statistics, 74, 152, *see also* Bayesian
  induction
Storage, *see* Memory
Subclass, 89
Subject, randomly chosen, 133, 146
Suicide note example, 164
Syntax, 6, 155

T

Tagging program, 153
Text analysis, *see* Content analysis
Thinking, cost of, *see* Cost factors
Turing machine, 131
Turing's test, 133, 144

U

Universe defined, 7, 13
User of CLS programs, 99

W

Weighting, 85, *see also* Linear weights
Wholist strategy, 22, 46